SUPER GHOSTS

Mark Ronson

Illustrated by Robin Lawrie

Beaver Books

First published in 1983 by
The Hamlyn Publishing Group Limited
London · New York · Sydney · Toronto
Astronaut House, Feltham, Middlesex, England

© Copyright Text Mark Ronson 1983
© Copyright Illustrations
The Hamlyn Publishing Group Limited 1983
ISBN 0 600 20628 9

Printed and bound in Great Britain by
Hazell Watson & Viney Limited, Aylesbury, Bucks

Set in Baskerville

For Charles and Cleo

Contents

Introduction

The ghosts you will read about in this book really are in the Super class – they have been chosen because they number among the most famous, or the strangest, of Britain's phantom population. Only supernatural stories connected with castles have been omitted as they have already been covered in the Beaver book *Haunted Castles*.

Some of the ghosts are rather frightening, some are sad, but others seem to be friendly and even playful. The fascinating thing about them all is that we still do not know what they are. Do psychical phenomena – which means supernatural happenings – actually take place, or are they only seen in the minds of specially sensitive people known as psychics? Are ghosts really the earthbound spirits of people who have died? Or are they 'echoes' from the past which, for some unknown reason, are 'replayed' at certain times like the re-running of an old film?

Several chapters feature haunted inns. Like castles and churches they are ideal 'haunts' as they are usually old and over the centuries have sheltered highwaymen, smugglers, persecuted priests and other fugitives as well as honest travellers – all of whom provide their share of phantoms. There are at least two hundred haunted inns in Britain, and in these pages you will find pub ghosts ranging from a skittle-playing monk to a smuggler with a terrible thirst.

The appearances of a few of the ghosts I have chosen may not be spectacular, but the stories behind them make up for this, as in the case of Dorothy Forster who is one of my favourite phantoms.

Super ghosts are those which are remembered

when lesser ones have been forgotten, and so our hauntings range over the last couple of centuries. Yet new hauntings are always occurring and reflect the times in which they take place. At the Bovington Tank Museum in Dorset the spectre of a German officer has been seen gazing at the Tiger tank he must have commanded in the Second World War. One of the most sensational series of manifestations in recent years occurred in the USA when the crew of a crashed aircraft appeared as ghosts in planes flying down the same Florida flight path as taken by the ill-fated Tri-Star. I am sure that some day there will be stories about a spectral spaceship.

Whatever ghosts may be, their stories have provided a great deal of entertainment. For many of us, one of the most enjoyable things to do is curl up with a book of scary stories and get the feeling that, if we were to look over our shoulders, we might see a shadowy *something*. It is not really ghosts which frighten us – we frighten ourselves with our own imaginations!

As I type this at midnight I wonder . . . is that a real footstep behind me?

Mark Ronson

Chapter 1
'A tall spindly fellow . . .'

'Oh, I am so glad we decided to live here,' said Amelia Cranswell as she watched the tip of the moon appear above the distant hills. 'It's just perfect.'

On this warm summer evening in 1875 Amelia and her two brothers, Edward and Michael, were sitting out on the lawn where they had enjoyed a picnic supper. Close to them a beck gurgled pleasantly and a soft breeze sighed through the avenue of ancient trees which led up to Croglin Low Hall. In such a peaceful setting none of the young people had an inkling of the nightmare that was soon to follow.

The Cranswells had come from Australia for a long visit the year before, and had found the old farmhouse, known as Croglin Low Hall, in Cumbria. The Fishers, who owned it, were moving to Thorncombe in Surrey and were pleased to lease it to them. The three young Australians soon made themselves popular among their neighbours as they settled down to enjoy English country life.

After watching the moonrise on this particular evening they went inside the grey stone house and wished each other goodnight. It was eleven o'clock when Amelia went into her ground-floor bedroom where she closed her window but not the shutters. She did not feel sleepy and sitting in bed she was able to look into the farmyard which was bathed in a mysterious silver light.

Slowly the girl became aware of two tiny glimmering lights in the shadows. At first she did not pay much attention to them – probably it was something reflecting the moon – but her interest suddenly increased as she realised that they were moving . . . coming nearer.

As they drew closer to her window Amelia thought they might be the yellowish eyes of some animal. No, they were too high above the ground to belong to a cat or a dog – they were at the same height as human eyes, *but human eyes do not glow in the dark*!

They vanished for a moment, then reappeared at the window and with a thrill of fear Amelia saw that they were gazing at her through the glass. Around them was the vague outline of a head, but it was too dark and indistinct to give the paralysed girl any hint of what sort of a creature it might be.

How long she and the unknown thing regarded each other Amelia could not say afterwards. It was a sound which released her from her trance – the unpleasant sound of nails scratching on glass. Fear of the mysterious figure made her roll out of bed and wrench at her door handle. It did not move, and she remembered she had followed her usual custom of turning the key in the lock.

All she had to do was turn it back and she could get away from that horrible scrabbling.

Quick! Quick! Not a moment to lose!

In her panic her fingers fumbled with the key and she heard it tinkle as it struck the stone floor. As she knelt and desperately ran her fingers over the flags in a blind search for it, a new sound came to her ears. Whatever it was that was trying to get in was unpicking the lead strips which held the glass panes. Glancing over her shoulder Amelia saw a face which looked as though it was made of wrinkled leather staring at her from the gap it had made in the panes.

Then, in the words of Captain Fisher, whose family owned Croglin Low Hall, 'a long bony finger of the creature came in and turned the handle of the window. The creature came in and twisted its long bony fingers into her hair, dragged her head over the side of the bed and bit her violently in the throat.'

Amelia became aware of low earnest voices.

'. . . and, gentlemen, I can only conclude that the creature which attacked your sister was some large monkey which has escaped from a travelling menagerie or that it was the work of a madman. Not long ago I had to attend a farmer's child who had been attacked in a similar fashion.'

The Australian girl opened her eyes and in the soft light of an oil lamp saw three figures standing at her bedside, her brothers and a man she recognised as the local doctor. She raised her hand to her neck and felt a bandage there, and then memory came flooding back.

She remembered screaming as the horrid thing clutched her, there were shouts from her brothers, who had been awakened by her cries, and the noise they made as they forced her lock with a poker.

After that she had fainted and her attacker had escaped through the open window as Michael and Edward burst into the room.

'I'm glad to say that the wounds are not deep,' the doctor was saying. 'More serious is the effect of such an attack on the young lady's mind. I would suggest that as soon as she is well enough to travel you take her away on a long holiday to forget her ordeal.'

So a few days later the Cranswells left the Cumbrian fells for the mountains of Switzerland. Here Amelia's terrifying experience began to fade from her mind as she and her brothers stayed in dreaming old lakeside towns and explored Alpine villages, so different from anything they had known in Australia. At last the time came to return to England, and Edward Cranswell asked his sister where she would like to live.

'Back at the Low Hall, of course!' she answered.

'But, after what happened . . .,' began Michael.

'It *was* frightening at the time but I am sure that it cannot happen again. If it was a monkey it could not survive long in the English countryside, and if it were a madman I am sure the poor thing has been locked up again by now.'

The two young men still looked doubtful.

'Look, we all love the Border country, we've made some friends on the neighbouring farms, and what is more we have a lease on the house.'

Her eagerness to return to Cumbria convinced them. When they got back to Croglin they found that life went on as though nothing unpleasant had happened, apart from two small differences – Amelia no longer locked her bedroom door but closed the shutters at night, and Edward slept with a pistol by him which he had bought in Switzerland.

The glorious Cumbrian autumn changed to bleak winter and the Cranswells continued their peaceful existence until one night in March 1876.

It was the nasty sound of fingernails scratching on glass which made Amelia sit bolt upright in bed. Somehow the intruder had forced the shutters and was trying to enter as it had the previous summer. Her cry brought Michael running to her room while, pistol in hand, Edward raced through a door into the farmyard which was lit by the moon riding in a sky of tattered cloud. At his sister's window he saw a form which he later described as 'a tall spindly fellow in a curious cloak'.

A light shone through the panes of glass as Michael came to his sister's aid. The thing at the window turned and ran through the stone archway above the entrance to the yard. Edward sprinted after the figure and saw it running between the trees bordering the drive which curved towards the Croglin road. He paused, raised his pistol and fired. In the moonlight he saw the enemy stagger, then continue jerkily across the narrow road and over the dark fields in the direction of Croglin village.

Not waiting to reload, Edward followed over the rough ground, tripping and blundering into dry-stone walls when clouds briefly hid the moon. He reached the edge of the village and had a final glimpse of the intruder disappearing into the old churchyard. Realising at last that he had to deal with the supernatural – with a vampire – Edward returned to Croglin Low Hall for his brother.

At dawn a small party – the two Cranswells, a couple of their neighbours and a gamekeeper – approached the village church. The ground was shrouded with mist out of which loomed old moss-covered tombs, and as they walked through the mist the men appeared to be cut off at the waist. No one spoke, but curious looks were cast at the Australians. Their story of a vampire sounded so impossible that, if they had not been well liked, their request for help would have been met with laughter.

As the searchers moved between the headstones the gamekeeper called out. The others crowded round a slab which was partly out of place. They heaved it to one side and muttered in horror at what they saw lying beneath it. Sprawled inside an ancient coffin was a tall mummified body with a circular hole in its thigh which Edward realised had been made by his bullet.

The men ran through the rusted gates, soon to return with armfuls of wood which they built into a bonfire in the far corner of the burial ground. As the sun rose like a golden disc through the mist they bent over the open grave and lifted out the skeletal form. Stumbling in their haste to be rid of their ghastly burden, they approached the blazing wood and heaved the Croglin vampire into the flames.

The story of Croglin Low Hall was written down by the Victorian author Augustus Hare in his book *My Solitary Life* (one volume of his autobiography *The Story of My Life*). It had been told to him by Captain Fisher.

While vampire legends are common in other parts of the world, especially east Europe, England has been mercifully free from these nightmarish creatures. There is only one other account of a vampire in England, and that goes back to the thirteenth century when it was believed that vampires were responsible for outbreaks of plague.

In his *Historia Rerum Anglicarum* the Chronicler William of Newburgh described how a master of Alnwick Castle in Northumberland – 'a stranger to God's grace and whose crimes were many' – returned from the dead to haunt the town which the castle protected. During the hours of darkness he would rise from his tomb to prowl the streets.

The local priest told William of Newburgh how this monster was followed by such a stench of decay that plague appeared in Alnwick and many people fled. Some men realised that the vampire was the cause of the pestilence and banded together to rid the town of the menace.

William wrote: 'They armed themselves, there-

12

fore, with sharp spades and betaking themselves to the cemetery, they began to dig. And whilst they yet thought they would have to dig much deeper, suddenly they came upon the body covered with but a thin layer of earth. It was gorged and swollen with a frightful corpulence. . . .'

One of the men struck the bloated body with the edge of his spade and from the wound came a gush of fresh blood, proving that indeed it was a vampire. Immediately it was taken outside the town and burned to ashes, after which no more people caught the plague.

Apart from the story of the vampire, Croglin has some other strange tales. One concerns its churchyard and a vicar who was there in the 1940s. He described his experience like this: 'I was coming down from Town Foot Farm in a snowstorm. It was about 9 p.m. and very dark and I had been for the milk. Just as I reached the churchyard wall my attention was taken by what appeared to be a funeral party in the portion reserved for the old rectors at the east end of the church. The figures were vague and diaphanous, and one of them I recognised.

'It only lasted a short time and I dismissed it from my mind as being imagination.

'About a week later one of the villagers suddenly died during a thunderstorm. The widow pleaded with me that he should be buried near the old rectors, and the spot finally chosen was that where I had seen the phenomenon. This is the only experience of a psychic nature that I have ever had – the figure I had recognised was that of the widow!'

Chapter 2

The mountain terror

Clammy mist swirled about the lone mountaineer as he picked his way down the stone-covered slope. Earlier in the day he had reached the cairn which stands on the summit of Ben Macdhui, the highest mountain in Scotland's Cairngorm range. As he began the return journey a curtain of white fog descended upon him. With it came an eerie silence.

The man moving cautiously in the mist was Norman Collie, a Professor of Chemistry at London University, and an enthusiastic climber. He felt no alarm at the sudden blotting out of the landscape — it had to be expected on Ben Macdhui. Having climbed the mountain before, he was confident that before long he would be enjoying supper in front of a log fire at his lodgings.

Suddenly he paused.

Through the eerie stillness came a faint sound. It reminded Professor Collie of a footstep, the crunch of someone stepping on the small stones which littered the slope. But that would be ridiculous. At the summit the view had been clear and he would have noticed any other mountaineers in the vicinity. He was convinced that he was the only one.

Crunch!

The professor knew that changes in temperature sometimes created a noise as rocks contracted or expanded, but such a sound was usually a sharp crack. No matter what explanation he could think of, he had to admit to himself that it could only be a footfall.

There it was again!

'This is nonsense,' the professor muttered to himself as a pang of fear shot through him. He began to hurry as the sound of more footsteps reached his ears.

He stopped and looked about him in the mist, but all he could see was a milky whiteness in each direction. Then, as he walked forward again, the mysterious sounds became more distinct.

'For every few steps I took I heard a crunch,' the professor was to relate afterwards, 'and then another crunch as if someone was walking after me but taking steps *three or four times the length of my own*!' He was seized with terror at the thought of something huge and unknown stalking him on the mountainside. He fled, racing down the slope, blundering into boulders which suddenly loomed up in the mist – and all the time aware of the crunching sound behind him.

At last he emerged from the mist above the Rothie-murchus Forest, and several miles from where he had begun his mad race. He was alone. Whatever it was that had inspired such panic in him was somewhere back in the mist.

This episode took place in 1891, but it was not until 1925 that the professor told his story publicly at a meeting of the Cairngorm Club in Aberdeen.

'Whatever you make of it I do not know,' he said, 'but there is something very queer about the top of Ben Macdhui and I will not go back there again by myself, I know!'

Reporters wrote about similar happenings which had been experienced on the mountain. One of the most interesting appeared in the Aberdeen *Press and Journal*, written by a Mr W. G. Robertson who had heard it from an old mountaineering friend named Henry Kellas.

Henry and his brother Dr A. M. Kellas, a very famous mountaineer who tragically lost his life on an Everest expedition, were below the summit of Ben Macdhui late one afternoon when suddenly they saw a giant figure coming down towards them from the cairn.

They saw it pass out of sight in a dip and, while waiting for it to reappear, were attacked by the same feeling of panic as Professor Collie.

'They were aware it was following them,' wrote Mr Robertson, 'and tore down by Coire Etchachan. Mr Kellas said there was mist on part of the hill, but refused to believe that the figure could be the shadow of either his brother or himself. He asked why not *two* figures if that had been the case. . . . No one who knew Mr Kellas or heard him relate his story could doubt his complete faith in his experience.'

Since then there have been many reports of the Big Grey Man as the apparition came to be named.

A typical example of the terror which the Big Grey Man inspired occurred on the mountain in 1945. One morning in May a mountaineer named Peter Densham, who had been employed on aircraft rescue work during the Second World War, set out from Aviemore and reached the summit of Ben Macdhui by midday. The weather was fine and clear but as he ate his packed lunch a heavy mist covered the mountain.

For a while he continued to eat in the moist silence, then he began to hear things . . . and remembered the strange tales. In the past he had not believed them, but now he felt that there was someone – or some thing – close to him. Then he heard a crunching noise from the direction of the cairn on his left.

Peter Densham later recalled how his thoughts turned to the Big Grey Man and the sound his footsteps were supposed to make. He was still not frightened, explaining that he thought the experience was interesting. But when the crunching was only yards away, he was engulfed by a sudden wave of panic and all he wanted to do was get off the mountain.

He began running wildly – and realised that he was fleeing towards Lurcher's Crag, a route which would end with him toppling to his death. He fought to halt his panic-stricken flight but found it impossible. It was as though there was a murderous force pushing him onwards. With a supreme effort of will, he managed to change direction. He raced down a ridge to the Allt Mor Bridge and on past Glenmore and only stopped running when he was on the other side of a loch.

A fascinating story of an encounter with the Big Grey Man – not just the sound of footsteps – is given in Richard Frere's book *Thoughts of a Mountaineer*. In order to win a bet a friend of his set himself an endurance test of spending a mid-winter night camped beside the Ben Macdhui cairn. During the night he awoke with a start of fear and a horrible sensation of being paralysed. As he lay still in his sleeping bag his eyes focused on a white patch on the wall of his tent. It was caused by a ray of moonlight coming through an opening in the fly-sheet, and as he watched a blurred shadow moved across it. *Something* was close at hand and had moved between his tent and the moon.

The man said afterwards that he felt he was in deadly danger, that whatever it was which had cast the shadow was hostile towards him. As he watched the shadow vanished, and this in some way released the tension which was paralysing him. Now his fear was mixed with curiosity and inch by inch he crawled out of his sleeping bag, parted the opening of the tent and gazed at the wild moonlit scene.

At a distance of about 18 metres he saw a huge creature 'swaggering' down a slope. It appeared to be covered with brown hair and had a head so large it was out of proportion to its body. The mountaineer said he was sure it was not some sort of ape because its arms were not long like those of a monkey.

A few moments later the figure vanished and the shivering man returned to his sleeping bag, trying to convince himself that what he had seen was a fellow climber wrapped up in bulky Alpine clothing. It seemed a pretty unlikely explanation, but it was the only one he could think of.

When the sun rose over the Cairngorms the man tried a simple but ingenious experiment to try and find out the height of the midnight prowler. There was no snow in the gully down which it had marched so there would be no footprints to give him a clue, but the mountaineer remembered that he had not been able to see the creature's feet while it passed a certain boulder which lay on the slope. This meant that it had been on the other side of the rock. He paced out the distance and reckoned it to be about 23 metres from his tent, then planted his ice axe by the boulder and returned to the opening of the tent.

When the creature's feet had been hidden by the boulder, its head had still appeared silhouetted just above the horizon. By making a comparison between the length of the ice axe, which stood nearly a metre above the ground, and the line of the horizon he was able to gain a rough indication of the creature's height. He said that he could not make it less than eight lengths of his axe and twice he made it ten, which meant that the figure was between seven and nine metres in height. It was exactly what he had thought at the time.

A story of an enormous creature roaming an icy Scottish peak in the middle of winter may seem fantastic, and even more so is the description of an encounter with the Big Grey Man which appeared in *The Scots Magazine* in June 1958. Here the author, a naturalist and climber named Alexander Tewnion, claimed that he had actually shot at it.

It was in 1943 when he had gone climbing in the Cairngorm Mountains in the hope of shooting some game to eke out wartime rations. On the afternoon he reached the summit of Ben Macdhui mist began to form in the pass below and a rising wind moaned in the rocks about him. His mountaineering instinct told him that a storm was approaching and, anxious to avoid it, he began to descend by what is known as the Coire Etchachan track. It was when he reached the mist that he heard the footsteps – footsteps with frighteningly long intervals between them.

Suddenly Tewnion found himself gazing at a huge shadowy shape looming up. For a moment it was hidden by the mist, then it was visible again – coming straight for him. He raised his gun and fired three times, then took to his heels and raced down the path to Glen Derry in a time he never bettered.

It would seem that the bullets did no harm to the Big Grey Man as sightings of him have increased since then. But the question remains – what is it that haunts Britain's second highest mountain? Could it be something – like the Loch Ness Monster – which has survived from a prehistoric age? Is it the *ghost* of some such creature which returns to the mountain over which it once roamed? Or is it a personification of an evil force?

It is an interesting point that those who have seen or heard the Big Grey Man admit to being filled with terror, and mountaineers are not easily frightened.

Such an attack of fear was described by Wendy Wood in her book *The Secret of Spey*. She was on the lower slope of the mountain when she heard an enormous, harsh voice echoing round her. She was too surprised to pick out the words, but she thought they sounded like Gaelic, the old language of the Scots.

At first she looked for some natural cause. Perhaps it was the barking of a deer magnified by a freak echo. Then it seemed the sounds were coming from beneath her feet. She searched the snow in a widening circle in case an injured climber lay beneath it and what she was hearing were his cries for help.

She found no one and the fear which she had been trying to keep in check suddenly overwhelmed her.

Her only thought was to get away. And as she ran from the spot she was certain that something sinister was following her. It took the same giant strides which had frightened Professor Collie. Stumbling desperately down the Lairig Ghru Pass she fled from those crunching footsteps without stopping for breath until she found herself near Whitewall.

Another woman to experience such a panic attack was the writer Joan Grant. One fine summer day in 1928 she was walking with her husband in the Rothiemurchus Forest, close to Ben Macdhui, when she was seized by a sensation of sheer horror. She turned and raced back along the path with her husband running after her, demanding to know what was wrong. All she could reply was that they must run faster, faster!

Afterwards she wrote that she knew that something evil was trying to reach her, and that if it did she would die.

'I had run about half a mile when I burst through an invisible barrier behind which I was safe,' she said. 'I knew I was safe now, though a second before I had been in mortal danger. A year later one of my Father's professors described an almost exactly similar experience when bug-hunting in the Cairngorms. . . . He had been so profoundly startled that he wrote to *The Times* – and received a letter from a reader who had also been pursued by the "thing".'

In her book *Time Out of Mind* Joan Grant wrote of a sinister sequel to her experience when some years later the local doctor told her that two lost hikers, for whom search parties had been out three days, had been found dead. He showed her the place on a large scale map and it was the exact spot where she had fled from the invisible menace.

Both men were in their twenties and had spent a good night under what is known as the Shelter Stone on the lower slope of Ben Macdhui. This was known because they had written their names and the date in a book which is kept there in water-proof wrapping. But after that no one knew what actually happened, though it was easy enough to guess. The searchers found their bodies within 90 metres of each other, sprawled face down as though death had struck them in headlong flight.

The doctor told Joan Grant that he had examined them and never in his life had he seen healthier corpses, not a thing being wrong with either of them except that their hearts had stopped.

'I put "heart failure" on the chit,' the doctor said, 'but it is my considered opinion that they died of fright.'

Chapter 3

The room-mate

'I haven't got a single room free,' said the sour-looking landlady of the Blue Posts inn. 'It's hard to get lodgings just now, what with the election and people waiting to board overdue ships. . . .'

'I'm aware of that, madam,' said Mr Hamilton wearily. 'The vessel on which I was supposed to take passage is still at sea, and I seem to have tramped the whole of Portsmouth seeking for a bed in vain. . . .'

'Well,' said the landlady thoughtfully, 'if you wouldn't mind sharing, there is a double room.'

'I wouldn't mind sharing with the Devil himself,' Mr Hamilton declared. 'Is my room-mate there?'

'No other person has it yet, but it'll be taken within the hour I'll be bound.'

'In that case, madam, I shall pay you for both beds and have the room to myself. I need a good night's rest.'

So it was agreed. The unsuspecting Mr Hamilton was led upstairs to a room where he looked at both beds and saw that one had what he described later as a 'decent counterpane' while the other was covered with a coarse patchwork quilt. He chose the bed with the counterpane – who knows what might have happened if he had taken the other – and, having locked the door to keep out intruders, lay down and slept.

We know what happened that night at the beginning of the last century at the Blue Posts because Mr Hamilton's account was recorded in the diary of a clergyman named Richard Harris Barham (the author of *The Ingoldsby Legends*) who added a note that 'it is one of the best authenticated ghost stories in existence'.

'I had slept I suppose an hour or more when I was awakened by a noise in the lane below,' Mr Hamilton recalled, 'but being convinced that it was merely occasioned by the breaking up of a jolly party, I was turning round to recompose myself, when I perceived, by the light of the moon which shone into the room, that the bed opposite was occupied by a man, having the appearance of a sailor.

'He was only partially undressed, having his trousers on, and what appeared, as well as I could make it out, to be a handkerchief, tied round his head by way of a nightcap. His position was half-sitting, half-reclining on the outside of the bed, and he seemed to be asleep.'

Mr Hamilton was angry that the landlady had broken the agreement after he had paid for both beds. At first he thought of making his room-mate leave but he was a kindly man and as the stranger was asleep he decided to let him rest, although he was determined to complain in the morning. He stared at the sailor for some time and noticed that he never made the slightest movement and was unaware of being watched. After a while Mr Hamilton closed his eyes and once more fell asleep.

'It was broad daylight when I awoke in the morning,' he continued, 'and the sun was shining full in through the window. My slumbering friend apparently had never moved, for there he was still, half-sitting, half-lying on the quilt, and I had a fair

23

opportunity of observing his features, which, though of a dark complexion, were not ill favoured, and were set off by a pair of bushy black whiskers. . . . What surprised me most, however, was that I could now plainly perceive that what I had taken in the moonlight for a red handkerchief on his forehead was in reality a white one, but quite saturated in parts with a crimson fluid, which trickled down his left cheek, and seemed to run upon the pillow.'

Mr Hamilton was puzzled as to how the stranger had entered the locked room, especially as he was certain no one was hiding there when he entered. He walked to the door to inspect the lock and found it fastened with the key in place just as he had left it. He decided to get an explanation from the sailor but, as he turned from the door, the stranger was not there.

'Scarcely an instant before I had observed him stretched in the same position which he had all along maintained,' Mr Hamilton related, 'and it was difficult to conceive how he had managed to make his exit so instantaneously, as it were, without my having perceived or heard him.'

He searched the room for a concealed exit, but could not find one. In an alarmed mood, he dressed and went downstairs.

At first he questioned the 'boots' who replied he 'knowed nothing of no sailors'. Then Mr Hamilton found the landlady, demanded his bill and told her he would not bother with breakfast as she had broken the agreement over the privacy of his room. At this her face flushed and she demanded what he meant but before he could answer she continued indignantly, 'You asked for the whole room and you had the whole room and though I say it, there is not a more comfortable room in Portsmouth. I might have let the spare bed five times over, and refused to do so because you asked me. Do you think to bilk me?'

He stopped her flow of angry words by placing a guinea on the bar, explaining that he was not complaining about his fellow lodger, but as he had paid double he expected the agreement to be kept. He now believed that it was some member of the staff who had let the man into his room without the landlady knowing.

'There was no one in your room unless you let him in yourself,' she said. 'Did you not have the key and did not I hear you lock the door after you?'

'But there certainly was a man – a sailor – in my room last night,' said Mr Hamilton, 'though I know no more how he got in or out than I do where he got his broken head, or his amazing whiskers.'

At these words the landlady went pale.

'I hesitated,' Mr Hamilton continued in his account, 'and at length a single word, uttered distinctly but lowly, as if breathlessly spoken, fell upon my ear; it was "Whiskers!"

'"Yes, whiskers," I replied, "I never saw so splendid a pair in my life."

'"Tell me exactly what happened," said the landlady.'

Surprised that the word 'whiskers' should have such an effect, Mr Hamilton described the sailor, adding that he must have gone there to sleep off his grog because although he had been knocked about, he did not appear to be aware of his condition. . . .

'Lord have mercy upon me!' the woman cried in terror. 'It's all true and the house is ruined forever!'

After begging her guest not to inform the authorities, she explained that three nights before his arrival a party of sailors were drinking at the inn. A quarrel broke out between them and some marines and angry words soon led to blows.

'The landlady in vain endeavoured to interfere,' Mr Hamilton explained, 'but a heavy blow, struck with the edge of a pewter pot, lighting upon the temple of a stout young fellow of five and twenty, who was one of the most active on the side of the sailors, brought him to the ground senseless and covered with blood.

'He never spoke again, but although his friends immediately conveyed him upstairs and placed him on the bed, endeavouring to staunch the blood and doing all in their power to save him, he breathed his last in a few minutes.

'In order to hush up the matter which would bring trouble to all concerned, the landlady agreed to the body being buried in the garden. The sailors and marines considered that, as he had just been paid off, no enquiry for him would take place.

'"But it was all for no use," the landlady said, wringing her hands. "Foul deeds will rise, and I shall never dare to put anyone in your room again, for there it was he was carried. They took off his jacket and waistcoat, and tied his wound up with a handkerchief, but they never could stop the bleeding till all was over. As sure as you are standing there a living man, he is come back to trouble us, for if he had been sitting to you for his picture, you could not have described him more accurately than you have done."'

An echo of the affair was reported in the *Star* newspaper on 21 February 1938.

Under the headline of MEMORY OF MURDER 200 YEARS AGO, a reporter told how a tombstone had been set up in the little courtyard where the sailor was supposed to have been buried. The story ended: 'To appease the ghost and to make up for his not being buried in consecrated ground, flowers were frequently placed on the spot where his bones were supposed to lie. Now the present landlady has gone a step further by placing there a tombstone.'

Chapter 4

The most haunted house

Two small boys crept up the weed-grown drive towards the burnt-out old house.

'My Mum would go mad if she knew I was here,' said one as they neared the open front door. 'She told me never to come near the place.'

'She won't find out, Ted,' said his companion. 'Anyway, I'm sure the fire drove all the old spooks away. 'Course, if you're scared. . . .'

'I'm not scared!' young Edward Rowling answered in a hushed voice. 'Let's take a look inside . . . and then perhaps we'd better go.'

'If you're not scared, you can go first.'

'Oh, all right.'

With his heart beating fast, Edward stepped up to the open door, edged past it and found himself in a hallway, the walls of which were blackened with smoke. A sour smell which comes from the sodden ashes of burned houses filled the air. The only sound was their footsteps.

In front of the boys was a staircase, a staircase so damaged by fire that it would be dangerous to tread on it. No wonder Edward had been told not to play in the ruins of Borley Rectory.

'C'mon, Ted, let's explore the rooms. . . .'

At that moment both boys looked up the stairs and saw a brass candlestick appear above the landing as though held by an unseen person. Next second it came hurtling down the stairway.

'The immediate action of myself and my companion was to put as great a distance between ourselves and Borley Rectory as we could in the shortest time,' Mr Rowling says today. 'On regaining our breath I remember being horrified at the suggestion made by my companion that we should pay the rectory another visit. Needless to say I declined the offer and took no part in any further visits.'

What is interesting about Mr Rowling's experience is it proved that, even though Borley Rectory had burned down, the strange forces which had haunted it for so long still lingered on.

Before the Second World War the rectory, which stood on the outskirts of Borley village in Essex, was known as 'the Most Haunted House in England'. At one stage in its history coaches regularly took sightseers to gaze at it, and hundreds of newspaper articles and several books were written about it. It has been estimated that over two hundred people experienced supernatural happenings there.

Borley Rectory was made famous by a ghost-hunter named Harry Price. Since his death some people have claimed that he exaggerated the happenings there, or even faked them, for the sake of publicity. Others have written in his defence and the arguments continue, but what must be remembered is that the rectory was well and truly haunted long before Harry Price appeared on the scene.

The history of the house, and its amazing assortment of ghosts, goes back to 1863 when it was built by the Reverend Henry Dawson Ellis Bull across the road from the twelfth-century Borley Church. He and his wife had fourteen children, and as his family increased he extended the house so that it became the rambling building which, in old photographs, appears exactly as you would imagine a haunted house.

The rectory had a large garden with a summerhouse at the far end. It had been built so the clergyman and his wife could sit in comfort while watching for the phantom nun. She was believed to appear on the long path following the southern boundary of the garden which was known as the Nun's Walk.

The Reverend Bull learned the legend of the nun from his parishioners. The story was that long ago a monastery stood on the rectory site and one of the monks fell in love with a young nun at a convent in nearby Bures in Suffolk. In the traditional way the lovers eloped in a coach but their freedom did not last long. They were caught by Church authorities and, for the breaking of their vows, the monk was hanged and the nun bricked up alive in the monastery foundations.

It was a splendid story to explain a haunting – the only trouble was that there was not a scrap of historical evidence to back it up. Later a medium received a 'spirit message' at the rectory and declared that the ghostly nun had been a French girl named Marie Lairre who had been murdered by drowning at Borley in 1667.

Whatever the story behind the phantom nun, her appearances were well known to the Reverend Bull and his family. He died in 1892 and he was succeeded as rector by his son, the Reverend Harry Foyster Bull, who was quite familiar with the Borley ghosts. He was a jolly, likeable man who had between twenty and thirty pet cats – all of whose names he remembered – who prowled after him when he strolled in the haunted garden. Not only did he see the phantom nun, but a ghostly coach which was drawn by two horses.

The most spectacular of these early sightings occurred in 1900 when the ghost was seen by four of the Bull sisters at the same time, such simultaneous sightings being rare. Three of the young ladies were standing by the summerhouse when they saw a robed figure gliding along the Nun's Walk. Two of them remained like statues by the summerhouse, but the third dashed into the house and called another sister to come out quickly. She did so, and when she saw the figure on the path it seemed so real she was not aware that she was in the presence of a spectre. She walked along the path as though to greet a real person – *and the figure melted away before her eyes!*

When the Reverend Harry Bull died his place was taken by the Reverend G. Eric Smith and his wife Mabel who moved into the rectory on 2 October 1928. They were to stay for only nine months, but it was through them that Borley achieved its fame.

The Smiths were soon aware there was something very uncanny about their new home. Those who had lived there before them had taken the Borley hauntings in their stride, but the new residents were scared by the supernatural happenings. Finally the vicar sought the advice of the *Daily Mirror*. The editor had an instinct for a good story and sent one of his best staff reporters to the little village.

On 10 June 1929, readers of the *Daily Mirror* opened the paper and read an article which began: 'Ghostly figures of headless coachmen and a nun, an old-time coach, drawn by two bay horses, which appears and vanishes mysteriously, and dragging footsteps in empty rooms. All these ingredients of a first-class ghost story are awaiting investigation by psychic experts. . . .'

The *Daily Mirror* editor wasted no time in finding a psychic expert to investigate the rectory. Two days later Harry Price arrived in Borley, and the Smiths told him how they had experienced eerie whispering sounds, mysterious footfalls and bells rung by unseen hands. Keys had mysteriously shot out of locks, and a vase had 'flown' from an upstairs window ledge and hurtled down the stairs (like the candlestick when young Edward Rowling entered the hall many years later). Two maidservants claimed to have seen apparitions, one saying that she had glimpsed the phantom coach which had been seen earlier by the Reverend Harry Bull.

Perhaps the strangest thing reported to Harry Price was a window which appeared to be lit up from the outside although the room behind it was always found to be in darkness.

The Smiths left Borley Rectory to its ghosts. The house stood empty for six months after which it became the home of the Reverend Lionel Foyster and his wife Marianne. It was during the five years they were there that the supernatural manifestations became sensational. The clergyman kept a diary of them, and later allowed Harry Price to quote from it in his book on Borley Rectory.

Scribbled messages – said to be written by a spirit – appeared on the walls addressed to Marianne asking for 'Mass', 'Light' and 'Prayers'. An unknown force frequently pealed the house bells and scattered showers of stones about the house. Two Church of England priests performed a service of exorcism in an attempt to quieten things down but the unearthly happenings continued.

The Foysters moved from Borley in October 1935, and in May 1937 Harry Price rented it for a year. He advertised in *The Times* for a number of investigators to stay at the rectory in groups and report on their experiences. Out of two hundred applications he selected forty people who visited Borley on a rota system. During this period details of the murdered nun 'came across' through the use of a planchette board – a device which holds a pencil and is used to receive 'spirit writing'.

The last living tenant of Borley Rectory was a Captain Gregson who, like those before him, experienced ghostly manifestations.

On 27 February 1939 – in line with a prophecy received by a medium – the rectory was gutted by fire. But it was far from the end of the Borley story. During the fire figures were seen at the upper windows of the blazing house even though Captain Gregson was the only occupant at the time.

In 1943 Harry Price began excavating the cellar of the burnt-out shell in hope of learning more about the Borley mystery. When the dig reached a depth of one metre a skull was found which an expert identified as being human and female. It was given proper burial in Liston churchyard in 1945, but the fascinating question remained – had Harry Price located the burial place of the murdered nun?

The following year the ruins of the house were demolished and today visitors to the rectory site are often disappointed when they find nothing there. What they may not realise is that across the road in Borley church the ghostly tradition continues.

One of the first to talk openly about the odd happenings in the church was the Reverend Harry Bull. He said that one day he and a friend were inside it when they both heard a tapping sound outside. It was so clear that the men followed it as it moved about the building. Afterwards they went outside but found nothing to explain the cause of the knocks. Since then there have been many instances of people hearing tapping both inside and outside the church.

Other phenomena have included the ringing of the church bell and the sounds of chanting and organ music – when the church has been securely bolted!

A feature of the hauntings is the mysterious movement of objects within the church. An example occurred when Mrs Harry Bull, revisiting Borley in 1947, offered to do the flower decorations for Easter Sunday. On the Saturday the rector congratulated her on her work, but next morning the flowers were strewn about the church as though hurled by an angry force. The blame could not be laid on vandals as the church had been locked and there were no signs of anyone having forced an entry.

In August 1949, the Reverend Stanley Kipling arrived at Borley church to take a service. Having changed into his gown in the vestry, he went to the porch where he was astonished to see a veiled female figure in the churchyard. As he watched it passed behind one of the yew trees, reappeared and then vanished. He rushed to the spot but – as one would expect at Borley – there was nothing to explain the brief materialisation. Until that moment he had not believed in the Borley ghosts, but from then on he was convinced of their existence.

Again in 1949 two young men, fascinated by the local tales of the haunted church, visited it one October night. While sheltering in the porch they heard curious sounds coming from inside. These were followed at twelve minutes to midnight by the appearance of a black figure moving silently towards the priest's door leading into the vestry before vanishing. . . .

The phantom nun was seen three times in the sixties by Terence Bacon who lived in a nearby cottage. He said she appeared to glide about 60cm above the grass and an interesting point is that the level of the churchyard used to be higher than it is today.

A 'shrouded figure walking down the church path' was seen by a psychic investigator watching for ghostly activity on the night of 20 June 1970. He used his walkie-talkie to call up two friends waiting nearby and soon the trio saw a light appear behind a chancel window which then moved slowly towards the altar. They checked that the church door was locked and that no one could be inside, and came to the conclusion that the light had not been carried by a living person.

It was an exciting night for the ghost-hunters. An hour and a half later the first investigator, now on the old rectory site, saw the phantom nun. She appeared to drift about 30cm above the ground, and when she came to a fence she passed through it as though it was not there. Using his radio the investigator warned his companions, who were on the road by the church, that the ghost was moving in their direction.

While they waited for her to appear a second walkie-talkie message told them she had passed back through the fence, crossed the old lawn and had stopped about 4.5 metres away. (In his report the investigator wrote that her face had a sad expression, her skin looked 'hard and dry' and her eyes were closed. Her garments were grey with something like a shawl on her head.)

Meanwhile the two men on the road separated, one going into the rectory garden. As he approached his friend he saw that there was a second figure, clothed in grey stuff, standing opposite him. . . .

Borley Rectory may have burned down over forty years ago but its ghosts continue to haunt the site.

Chapter 5

Ghost armies

'I tell you I did see them!'

Mocking laughter greeted these words and the farm labourer who had uttered them turned away angrily.

'Last night were Midsummer Eve an' I reckon he were bewitched,' said one of his mates.

'Befuddled more like,' chimed in another. 'You can be sure the only spirits he saw came out of a bottle!'

'You sound a mite too jolly to be working,' declared William Lancaster, striding into the yard. It was hay-making time at his farm at Blake Hills in Cumbria, and he was anxious to begin.

'What's all the fuss about?' he asked.

'Soldiers,' cried the labourer. 'Yesterday I saw soldiers up there. . . .' He pointed to where Souter Fell loomed against the summer sky.

'Soldiers, you say?' said William Lancaster. 'I've not heard of any militia hereabouts. And what would they be doing up on Souter?'

'I don't know, sir, but I saw them. It was getting on towards evening when I looked up and saw an army column marching from the north across the east side of the fell.'

He went on to say that at first there was nothing to suggest the soldiers he was watching were other than flesh and blood. But, as the column continued like a colourful snake across the fell top, it dawned on him that a normal army would have taken the easy route round the desolate hill.

William Lancaster snorted with disbelief.

'Ridiculous,' he said. 'What army would march over Souter Fell? Those north and west faces are sheer drops.'

'Perhaps an army of ghosts,' muttered the man as he and his fellow labourers trooped off to the fields.

William Lancaster had good cause to remember this incident two years later. On the afternoon of 23 June 1737, he happened to glance towards Souter Fell and saw some men walking with their horses. For a moment he thought it might be a hunting party, but when he looked again he saw the men had mounted and were riding at the head of an army marching five abreast.

The farmer called his family and they watched spellbound as the column divided into companies, each under the command of a mounted officer. As twilight gathered about the fell they saw that the discipline of the soldiers relaxed, they fell out of step and broke ranks. Then darkness hid them.

Next day William made the mistake of enthusiastically telling his story . . . and was ridiculed just as his labourer had been. Eight years were to pass before he and his family saw the mysterious army again, but this time he had the satisfaction of having his words proved.

The nineteenth-century writer Harriet Martineau was fascinated by the Souter Fell story and made a special study of it.

In her book *The English Lakes* she described the last appearance of the phantom army like this: 'On the

Midsummer-eve of the fearful 1745, twenty-six persons, expressly summoned by the [Lancaster] family, saw all that had been seen before, and more. Carriages were now interspersed with the troops; and everybody knew that no carriages had been, or could be, on the summit of Souter Fell. The multitude was beyond imagination; for the troops filled a space of a kilometre, and marched quickly till night hid them — still marching.

'There was nothing vaporous or indistinct about the appearance of these spectres. So real did they seem, that some of the people went up, the next morning, to look for the hoofmarks of the horses; and awful it was to them to find not one footprint on heather or grass.

'The witnesses attested the whole story on oath before a magistrate; and fearful were the expectations held by the whole countryside about the coming events of the Scotch rebellion.'

'The Scotch rebellion' was the 45, or Second Jacobite Rebellion. The Jacobite army, led by Bonnie Prince Charlie, entered England in the autumn of 1745, so it was not surprising that people in northern England that summer were fearful that the phantom army was about to become grim reality.

The odd thing about the Souter Fell phantoms is that nothing was known about them. It was not a re-enactment of something which happened in the past — no battle had been fought in the vicinity. Nor was it a glimpse of some future event, so far no army has marched over the fell. In contrast, England's most famous military ghosts were recognised by some of their old comrades when night after night they re-fought a battle in the sky above Edgehill.

The real Battle of Edgehill took place on 23 October 1642, and was the first serious fighting in the Civil

War. Both sides were equally matched, the Royalists and the Parliamentarians having about 13 500 troops, and at the end of the day both sides claimed the victory.

It seems the advantage went slightly to the Royalists, but total victory was thrown away by King Charles's nephew Prince Rupert. He led his cavaliers in a devastating charge but was so enthusiastic in the pursuit of fleeing Roundheads he forgot the battle. When the cavalry finally returned to the field it was too late to take advantage of their success.

By sundown the King had the opportunity of marching on London which, had he done so, would have probably altered the course of our history. But it was Charles's first taste of war and he was so distressed by the bloodshed he was unable to think clearly. His commanders could not agree on what to do and so the chance of winning the capital was lost forever.

Two months passed. Then, a few days before Christmas, a band of travellers found themselves at Edgehill just after midnight. Suddenly they heard drums. The unexpected sound puzzled them because in those days armies did not fight after dark. They shivered as the screams of invisible wounded rose above the rhythmic beat.

As one they turned to flee from the ominous noises – then they saw something so extraordinary they dared not move. Huddled behind hedges they watched while a battle scene materialised in the air above them.

Later they described how – with ensigns flying, drums rolling and muskets firing – an army followed the royal colours against a Parliamentarian force. At first the King's army seemed to be having the best of it, then the Roundheads rallied and had the advantage for a while. There could be no doubt that it was a supernatural re-enactment of the battle which had been recently fought there.

A report, published a month later, described how 'till two or three in the morning in equall scale continued this dreadful fight, the clattering of Armes, noyse of Cannons, cries of souldiers, so amazing and terrifying the poore men, that they could not believe they were mortall, or give credit to their eares and eyes; runne away they durst not, for feare of being made a prey to these infernall souldiers, and so they, with much fear and affright, stayed to behold the success of the business. . . .'

After they had been watching in terror for three hours, the travellers saw the vision fade. They knew that they had experienced something very remarkable and they now wanted to put it on record. They hurried to the town of Keinton (now Kineton) where they hammered on the door of a Justice of the Peace, William Wood, and when he appeared bleary-eyed they hustled him to his neighbour, the Reverend Samuel Marshall, in order to have their statements taken down under oath.

Soon afterwards the story of the phantom battle was published in a pamphlet which had the following title:

A Great Wonder in Heaven, showing the late Apparitions and Prodigious Noyses of War and Battels, seen on Edge-Hill, neere Keinton in Northamptonshire. – Certified under the Hands of WILLIAM WOOD, Esquire, and Justice for the Peace in the said Countie, SAMUEL MARSHALL, Preacher of GODS Word in Keinton, and other Persons of Qualitie.

The writer of the pamphlet described what happened after the first sighting. William Wood and the Reverend Marshall were very reluctant to believe the travellers at first – the story was so incredible that it sounded like something imagined by a madman or a drunkard. But they knew some of the travellers to be truthful and responsible people, and so: 'suspending their judgements till the next night about the same houre, they, with the same men, and all the substantial Inhabitants of that and the neighbouring parishes, drew thither; where, about halfe an houre after their arrivall, on Sunday, being Christmas night, appeared in the same tumultous warlike manner, the same two adverse Armies, fighting with as much spite and spleen as formerly: and so departed the gentlemen and all the spectators, much terrified with these visions of horrour, withdrew themselves to their houses, beseeching God to defend them from those hellish and prodigious enemies.'

On Boxing Day news of the supernatural battle sent people tramping along the frosty lanes in the direction of Edgehill, half hoping to see the phantoms and half afraid they would appear. But this night the sky remained empty. Through the week a dwindling band kept vigil at the battlefield and it was not until Saturday night that their patience was rewarded.

The first hint of the approaching battle was a stutter of drums, then once again phantom soldiers charged with flashing swords while guns spurted flame through rolling clouds of powder smoke.

The battle was repeated on the Sunday night, after which nothing happened until the following weekend. As word of the phenomenon spread further afield crowds flocked to Edgehill as though to an entertainment. Perhaps the fact that no spectators had come to harm reassured them, and one wonders if they got so carried away by the action that they cheered when the Cavaliers advanced or if Roundhead pikemen repelled an attack.

News of the 'Great Wonder' reached King Charles at his Oxford headquarters. He was so interested that he immediately dispatched a commission, made up of Colonel Lewis Kirke, Captain Dudley, Captain Wainman and three other gentlemen, to investigate. The party travelled to Keinton where they read the statement made to the Reverend Marshall and questioned witnesses.

On Saturday night they went to Edgehill to see the apparitions for themselves. They saw them again on Sunday and what amazed them was that they could recognise dead comrades including Sir Edmund Verney, the Royalist standard-bearer. The commission returned to Oxford and made a statement under oath to His Majesty that they had twice observed the phantom soldiers.

After that interest in Edgehill faded. England was torn by civil war and it was real battles which affected people's lives. But it was not the end of the haunting. Although the battle scenes have not been repeated, down the years to our own time groups of spectral soldiers have been glimpsed there.

Chapter 6
Pearlin Jean

As young Robert Stuart jolted from side to side he could not imagine a more dismal scene than the one beyond the mud-spattered windows of the ancient carriage. It was only mid-afternoon yet daylight was fading, grey mist hung over the slopes of heather-covered hills and frequently the landscape faded behind curtains of drizzle. Even the carriage was depressing. Painted black, it reminded him of a hearse, and the coachman, bent with age and cackling curses at the floundering horses, seemed more like an undertaker than a family servant he had known since boyhood.

'What a homecoming!' Robert sighed. 'I'd forgotten how grim Scotland can be!'

He sighed again, thinking of his travels along the hot roads of Italy, of the wine festivals he had enjoyed in quaint villages on the Rhine and, most of all, of his life in Paris. A tear rolled down his cheek.

Robert Stuart had grown up at his family home of Allanbank, an estate close to the village of Allanton in the Borders region of south-east Scotland. A couple of years earlier he had left it to go on the Grand Tour. This was a leisurely journey round Europe undertaken by young men of quality to complete their education.

During his travels Robert had done more than visit art galleries and museums. After his strict upbringing he had delighted in the free and easy life across the Channel. He had drunk wine, cheerfully lost his allowance at cards, chased after pretty girls – and now it was all over. Worse, when his father had written to him in Paris commanding him to return home, his great adventure had ended in a secret tragedy. As it all came back to him a second tear trickled down his handsome face.

'Ye'll soon be home now, young master,' called the coachman. 'Just a short way to go, if these nags don't drop dead first.' His whip cracked and the horses struggled harder to pull the creaking vehicle along a road little better than a muddy track.

Robert now saw the outlines of familiar trees which seemed to wave gaunt arms at him through the mist. Ahead was the wall which surrounded Allanbank, with a high arch over its gateway. Once he was through it he would have resign himself to a dull life helping his father manage the estate, but perhaps it would take his mind off what had happened in Paris. Perhaps it would be good to be home again after all.

The young man put his head out of the window to see his old home and a cry choked in his throat. On top of the arch he saw the figure of a girl dressed in a white dress made of a lace-like material which was known as 'pearlin' in Scotland. But what made Robert fall back into the carriage in a dead faint was the mask of blood which hid her face.

Fear came to Allanbank with the return of its heir. Robert's parents could not understand what ailed him. Often he was white-faced in the morning, his hands trembling after another sleepless night. But it was not only his nervous condition – had something frightening and uncanny returned with him? The servants whispered together about a cry that rang down the corridors of the old house at night, and of the rustling sounds of an invisible silky dress.

It was as though a ghost had followed the young man and, the servants were quick to notice, the manifestations stopped whenever he visited Edinburgh. To escape the unseen presence Robert spent more and more of his time in that city. This relief came to an end in 1687 when he inherited the baronetcy and had to stay at Allanbank to manage the estate.

Supernatural activity increased dramatically now he could no longer get away from the house. During the night an unseen power scattered the furniture, and members of the household shuddered in their beds as doors – which they had carefully bolted – opened and slammed.

The disturbances reached a climax when Sir Robert brought a wife to Allanbank. The new Lady Stuart spent a night with cries echoing outside her bedroom and doors rattling as though a storm blew through the house.

'My dear, I think you should explain to me what this nocturnal commotion is about,' she said to Sir Robert. 'Whatever it is, I promise to stand by you and help you overcome it.'

'Then I must confess to you something which still makes me shudder to think of,' he said. 'It began when I was living in Paris. . . .'

He explained that he had lodged in a house over-looking a convent garden where novices – girls who had not yet taken their final vows to become nuns – were allowed to stroll after their religious studies. One in particular caught his eye because of her large blue eyes and a hint of lovely blonde hair hidden beneath her starched head-dress. He found out that her name was Jeanne de la Salle. She was a romantic young woman who had decided to become a nun on an impulse, only to find it impossible to forget the pleasures of the outside world.

When she looked up from the walled garden and saw the handsome young Scot gazing at her with a lovelorn expression she gave him such a warm smile that his heart hammered. Soon they were smuggling notes to each other and a few weeks later Mademoiselle de la Salle caused a scandal at the convent by running away with Robert Stuart.

They took lodgings together and Jeanne was confident that Robert would soon make her his wife. He allowed her to go on thinking this, not wishing to tell her that marriage was out of the question. His stern father would never give him permission to marry a French girl – his son must wed a girl of an aristocratic Scottish family. And if Robert were to marry without his father's consent he knew that he would be cut off with a groat. So he said nothing and the weeks passed happily for them both.

One day a letter reached Robert from his father stating that he had been abroad long enough and he must return immediately to Allanbank.

Robert knew that to disobey the old baronet was to put his inheritance at risk. He had to return to Scotland, but what about Jeanne. He did not have the courage to tell her the truth and even on the morning of his departure he did not explain what was happening. When the coach came to take him on his journey he strode out of the house in moody silence and climbed into the vehicle.

Realising that her lover was abandoning her, Jeanne de la Salle ran into the street and implored him to stay with her in Paris or take her back to

Scotland as his bride. Robert cringed at the public scene and called to the coachman to whip up the horses. At this Jeanne put her foot on the hub of the front wheel and tried to climb in, still begging Robert not to leave her.

'Drive off, you fool!' he shouted to the bewildered driver.

'Robert Stuart, if you marry any woman but me I shall come between you and her to the end of your days!' cried Jeanne.

The coachman's whip cracked like a gunshot. The vehicle lurched forward and the girl was hurled to the ground. A carriage wheel passed over her head and blood dyed her white pearlin dress.

'I saw her waiting for me on the arch when I returned to Allanbank,' Robert told his wife. 'Until now I have kept that terrible happening in Paris a secret, but there is no doubt about it that Jeanne is haunting me.'

The young woman liked being Lady Stuart and she was determined that no jealous ghost was going to drive her away from her new home.

'Do not worry, Robert,' she said. 'There are ways of dealing with these things. We shall have this annoying phantom banished.'

Seven ministers of the Church of Scotland were invited to Allanbank to perform a service of exorcism – a religious ritual for 'casting out' spirits – but their prayers were to no avail. Pearlin Jean not only remained but increased her persecution of the newly-married couple.

'Robert Stuart, if you marry any woman but me I will come between you and her to the end of your days!'

The last words of Jeanne de la Salle returned to Sir Robert's mind and he had a strange idea which might just put an end to the haunting. He hired an artist to paint a portrait of Jeanne from a description he gave him. When the picture was finished it was hung between a painting of Sir Robert and one of Lady Stuart. This symbolic gesture seems to have satisfied the ghost for at last Allenbank was peaceful. Sir Robert and his wife had several children. When they grew older Lady Stuart decided to banish the picture of Jeanne de la Salle to a lumber room so she would not have to answer embarrassing questions about the lady hanging between Mama and Papa.

Within minutes of the portrait being taken down the angry ghost returned and Allanbank continued to be one of Scotland's most haunted houses. Even after Sir Robert and his wife died, eerie happenings continued and many were the stories told about Pearlin Jean. Her spectre, with its blood-stained head, was frequently seen in the grounds.

In the nineteenth century the old house was pulled down and people thought it would be the end of the jilted ghost. But for a long time afterwards Pearlin Jean was glimpsed, usually at dusk, in the overgrown garden where Allanbank had stood. On one occasion a young man named Thomas Blackadder, waiting in the orchard for his girlfriend, went towards the figure of a young woman which appeared through the trees. Only when it faded before his outstretched arms did he realise he had tried to embrace Pearlin Jean.

Chapter 7
Theophilus Brome and company

'Here's to us, lads, and to old Theophilus,' shouted the tipsy foreman as he poured the contents of a bottle into the upside-down skull. 'I reckon the ancient gent won't mind me using his headpiece as a goblet seeing we done such a good job on his house. . . .'

'You shouldn't be doing that,' said a maidservant pushing through the ring of guffawing workmen. 'They do say dreadful things happen if that skull ain't treated with respect.'

The foreman lowered the skull from his lips.

'This is 1826!' he declared. 'You ain't in the Middle Ages, girl, when folk believed such superstitious rubbish. Now, who wants the next swig?'

Eager hands reached forward – it would be a good tale to tell how the completion of the renovations at Higher Chilton Farm was celebrated by drinking from its famous skull.

Suddenly the laughter died and the maidservant gave a little shriek as a low moaning sound was heard. It seemed to come from the very air about them.

'It's Theophilus!' cried the girl. 'I warned you. . . .'

Again the sound was heard. Low at first, it rose like some sudden moaning wind, full of menace and anger. A couple of Catholics in the party made the Sign of the Cross and the foreman — suddenly sober — lowered the skull with ale spilling from its empty eye sockets.

The moaning gradually died. It was followed by a silence which no one dared break. All eyes focused on the highly polished skull as though hypnotised by it. Slowly the men backed away.

When the unearthly noise came again it was as though an angry voice was magnified and distorted. As it re-echoed through the farmhouse the actual words were blurred but their meaning was clear — the voice was uttering a curse. Led by the foreman, the builders bolted for the door. Once outside they ran from the farm and its angry spirit until they had no breath left.

Today the skull of Theophilus Brome is treated with care and respect at the Somerset village of Chilton Cantelo. Higher Chilton Farm stands opposite the church where the headless body of Theophilus Brome was buried in the north transept in August 1670. For some unknown reason he requested that his skull should remain permanently in the farmhouse which was his home after his arrival from Warwickshire.

There were rumours that he had been involved in the Civil War and had come to the south to escape retribution. After the Restoration there were cases of dead enemies of the monarchy having their coffins opened and their heads removed as symbolic punishment. (Oliver Cromwell's body was hung in chains at Tyburn and his head stuck on a spike at Westminster.) Perhaps it was to avoid such treatment after his death that Theophilus left such an unusual request in his will.

For over three centuries the skull has remained in the farmhouse, not because the various tenants wanted it there but because they were afraid to move it. If the skull was interfered with so terrifying were the disturbances which followed that it was hastily returned to its special closet.

One example of the skull's ability to make its anger felt was described in Victorian times in Collinson's *History of Somerset* like this: 'The tenants of the house have often endeavoured to commit [the skull] to the bowels of the earth, but have as often been deterred by horrid noises portentive of sad displeasure; and about twenty years since (which was perhaps the last attempt) the sexton, in digging a place for the skull's repository, broke the spade in two pieces, and uttered a solemn asseveration never more to attempt an act so evidently repugnant to the quiet of Brome's Head.'

The wife of the present owner of Higher Chilton Farm finds that having the skull of Theophilus under her roof is not alarming if it is treated correctly.

'People expect me to be frightened,' she says, 'but I know that, provided he is not taken outside the house, he would never do me any harm. As long as he is treated with respect he never causes trouble.'

Skull haunting is one of the strangest aspects of the British supernatural scene. There are several houses and stately homes with skulls which, like that of Theophilus Brome, cause terrifying manifestations if they are disturbed. Some are even said to scream.

The most frightening of all these skull stories took place in Cumbria. Today Calgarth Hall, a sixteenth-century manor house standing close to the shore of Lake Windermere, is one of the most pleasant guest houses you could find, and has no hint of the two vengeful skulls which once haunted it.

The story goes back to when the land surrounding the hall was farmed by Kraster Cook and his wife Dorothy. Their small farm bordered the estate of a wealthy magistrate named Myles Phillipson who coveted the Cooks' land, wishing to build a new manor house there. Kraster Cook resolutely held out against Phillipson's tempting offers, and this greatly angered him.

Just before Christmas, Phillipson rode over to the Cooks' humble farmhouse and, with a jovial smile, said that as it was the season of goodwill they should let bygones be bygones. To prove he was sincere he invited the couple to his home for Christmas dinner.

Kraster and Dorothy were awed by the invitation but were also greatly relieved – Myles Phillipson had the reputation of being a dangerous enemy. They accepted politely, and on Christmas morning arrived at the Phillipsons' house were, conscious of their plain clothing, they mingled uncomfortably with the fashionable guests. At dinner the farmer could think of nothing to say to those seated about him, and in his embarrassment he fixed his gaze on a silver bowl.

'I see that you greatly admire that bowl,' said Phillipson's wife in a voice loud enough to carry through the room. 'Well, it's worth any man's admiration.'

When the long meal was over and the Cooks were about to depart gratefully there was a sudden commotion. Glowering with anger, Myles Phillipson shouted that his precious silver bowl had been stolen. To allay unpleasant suspicions, the guests consented to be searched. Kraster and Dorothy had just buttoned themselves into their outer garments, which had been left hanging by the entrance. When their turn came to be searched the silver vessel was found in one of their pockets.

In the uproar which followed the guests reminded

each other how the uncouth farmer had eyed the bowl during the banquet. The bewildered couple were arrested and their muttered protestations of innocence were ignored by the jeering guests.

They were tried before Magistrate Phillipson and – as theft could carry the death penalty in those days – he lost little time in sentencing them to be hanged.

When he finished his dread pronouncement, Dorothy Cook shouted at him, 'Guard thyself, Myles Phillipson! Thou thinkest thou has managed grandly, but that tiny lump of land is the dearest a Phillipson has ever bought or stolen, for you will never prosper, neither will your breed. Whatever scheme you undertake will wither in your hand; the side you take will always lose; the time shall come when no Phillipson shall own an inch of land; and while Calgarth walls shall stand we'll haunt you night and day. Never will ye be rid of us!'

The bodies of Kraster and Dorothy were still dangling in irons when the Phillipsons took over their farm, demolished the old farmhouse and ordered work to begin on Calgarth Hall.

By next Christmas it was ready and a grand banquet was planned to celebrate its completion. During the feast Phillipson's wife went upstairs to her bedroom. As she ascended the staircase, she suddenly shrieked. Back in the dining hall she babbled that she had seen two leering skulls perched on the balustrade. One still had hair . . . hair like the hanged Dorothy Cook!

The guests jostled to the bottom of the stairs and, just as their hostess had described, there were two skulls. A man drew his sword and nervously tapped one with the point. It was solid enough, and with sudden relief it was decided that the whole thing was a joke in bad taste. The skulls were hurled into the night. A servant who had reason to have a grudge against his master was accused of the trick and locked in a cellar but his innocence was soon to be proved.

After the guests had retired for the night, Calgarth Hall echoed with ghastly shrieks. When a frightened crowd gathered at the staircase it was seen that the skulls had returned to their original position. The curse of Dorothy Cook was recalled in whispers, and when the sun rose the guests were eager to depart.

As the clopping of horses and the creak of carriages faded away, Myles Phillipson tossed the skulls into the duck pond. But he knew that this was no answer and that the skulls would return to the staircase – which they did night after night.

From then on Myles Phillipson suffered a series of misfortunes, and it seemed to him that each setback was accompanied by wilder screams from the skulls. His position and lands were lost, and when he died he only had Calgarth Hall to leave to his son.

The skulls now appeared only at Christmas time and on the anniversary of the Cooks' execution. But the power of the curse continued to plague the Phillipson family until it sank into poverty and oblivion, and the hall passed into other hands.

All that remained of the man who had built the hall was his coat of arms on one of the fireplaces. With the curse fulfilled the skulls quit the scene of their haunting for ever.

Unlike the skulls of Calgarth Hall, a skull known as 'Dickie' was very friendly towards its hosts who lived in Tunstead Farm overlooking Coomb's Reservoir in the Peak District of Derbyshire. At one time Dickie was even pictured on local postcards, grinning from a window ledge which was its favourite resting place. Like the skull of Theophilus Brome, Dickie was quite peaceful until any attempt was made to evict him from the house.

In his book *Tour through the High Peak* the Victorian author John Hutchinson wrote: '. . . I have been informed by a credible person, a Mr Adam Fox, who was brought up in the house, that he has not only repeatedly heard singular noises, and observed very extraordinary circumstances, but can produce fifty persons, within the parish, who have seen an apparition at this place.

'He has often found the doors opening to his hand – the servants have been repeatedly called up in the morning – many good offices have been done by the apparition, at different times – and, in fact, it is looked upon more as a guardian spirit, than a terror to the family – never disturbing them but in case of an approaching death of a relation or neighbour, and shewing its resentment only when spoken of with disrespect, or when its own awful memorial of mortality is removed.

'For twice within the memory of man, the skull has been taken from the premises, once on building the present house on the site of the old one, and another time when it was buried in Chapel-en-le-Frith church yard – but there was no peace – no rest – it must be replaced!'

The original owner of the skull is believed to have been a soldier named Ned Dickson who left Tunstead Farm for France to fight in the Huguenot Wars. In 1590, after being badly wounded at the Battle of Ivry, he returned to Derbyshire to live on his property.

When he arrived at the farm he found that a cousin and his wife, having eagerly believed a rumour that he had died of his wounds, had taken it over for themselves. The welcome they gave the ex-soldier

54

was far from cordial though they did invite him to stay the night.

Ned Dickson was never seen again. The suspicion that he had been murdered in his bed was confirmed when the cousin's wife saw Dickie's skull grinning at her. It had returned to its rightful inheritance to drive away the murderers.

Once the skull was back at the farm it had no intention of leaving again.

J. Castle Hall, an author who studied the story, wrote: 'According to the evidence of many local inhabitants, the house is peaceful and quiet while the skull remains there, but if it be removed . . . a voice is heard in the wind as the latter, with strange moanings, comes through the keyholes of every door in the house, saying, "Fetch poor Dickie back . . . Fetch poor Dickie back . . ." and to this day the weird skull rests in the quiet corner of the window, and in the room a peculiar silence reigns.'

Although this 'voice in the wind' was frightening, most of the time Dickie acted as a supernatural guardian of the farm. When an animal was ill, and especially during the lambing season, the farmer could rely on Dickie to call him out if he was needed.

The summons was always three light taps on the window pane. It even acted as an alarm clock for sleepy servants, and on one occasion roused a tenant farmer in time to save the life of a cow which was being accidentally strangled by a length of chain. Once a thief came to Tunstead in the night, but he was speedily caught after Dickie set the house vibrating with thumps and bangs.

Dickie's greatest triumph was in getting the course of a railway altered. It happened during the construction of the London and North Western line which was to run between Buxton and Stockport. The railway engineers wanted to push it across part of Tunstead Farm, and when the owner objected compulsory powers were obtained and work began on making a track over the disputed land.

At one point it was necessary to make a bridge and an embankment, but every time work began the earth slipped and the disgruntled labourers would have to start digging all over again. Finally the engineers realised that they were never going to complete the link through Tunstead Farm and diverted the line, giving as an excuse 'the unstable nature of the ground'.

The local people knew that it was really the work of Dickie, once again protecting the interests of the farm. The skull's role in the affair was acknowledged when a bridge on the railway line was officially named Dickie's Bridge – a name still to be seen on large-scale maps of the area.

Apart from these three cases, there are several other skull hauntings in England, and it seems all the skulls have the same objection to being moved. At Flagg Hall in Derbyshire a skull was kept in a glass case. It is believed that it was once the property of a doctor who rented the hall, and who obtained the skull for medical studies from a body-snatcher. One day the owners of the hall made a determined effort to give the skull a Christian burial in the Chelmorton churchyard. Before the hearse carrying it reached the church the horses halted as though held back by an invisible wall. Nothing would persuade them to move until the undertaker pulled their heads round and headed back to Flagg Hall.

The skull at Wardley Hall, which stands just north of Salford in Greater Manchester, was once protected by a special clause in the lease. The owner of the skull is thought to have been a Catholic priest named

Father Ambrose who, in the days of religious persecution, was executed at Lancaster Castle.

After his head was exhibited at a Manchester church, it was smuggled to the hall which was owned by his Catholic friends. Terrifying manifestations took place when later tenants of the house tried to get rid of it.

A stately home which has England's most famous haunting skull is Burton Agnes Hall, near the village of Burton Agnes in Humberside. Its story goes back to the reign of Elizabeth I when Sir Henry Griffith began building the house. His three daughters shared his love for the project and after his death they devoted themselves to finishing his work. Of the sisters the one most enthusiastic for the project was Anne. Tragically, after the house was finished in 1620, she was killed by robbers. As she lay dying she implored her sisters to keep her head safely in the house so that part of her would remain there forever.

The request was put down to a disturbed mind and Anne's sisters had her buried in the family vault. Soon the house echoed with crashes, low groans were heard in its corridors, doors were slammed by invisible forces, and for nights on end sleep was impossible. Finally Anne's last request was carried out and her skull was brought into the house.

If you visit Burton Agnes Hall you will see a portrait of Anne Griffiths and her sisters hanging above a staircase. Her skull is thought to be hidden behind an ancient screen.

Chapter 8
Bumps in the night

It was the yelping of a dog which made Miss Freer's eyes snap open.

'Spooks, what is it?' she called to her terrified Pomeranian, at the same time reaching towards the bedside table to light her candle. She was an experienced psychic investigator but, as the candle flame grew around its wick, she was not prepared for what had made Spooks go rigid with terror. On the table top close to her bed were two black paws – *and nothing else!*

In describing the ghostly dog which was invisible except for its forefeet, she wrote understandably: 'It gave me a sickening sensation.'

Ada Goodrich-Freer was investigating Ballechin House in Perthshire which, at the end of the last century, had gained the reputation of being Scotland's most haunted mansion. The black paws were only one of the many extraordinary happenings which she and her fellow ghost-hunters experienced.

Ballechin's uncanny history goes back to 1806 when the house was built on an estate which had been owned by the Steuart family for three centuries. It had been planned to replace the original manor house, and the same year Robert Steuart, the heir to the estate, was born. At the age of nineteen he joined the East India Company's militia, and twenty-five years later retired to Ballechin.

It was soon the gossip of the district that Robert had come back from India a very eccentric man. For one thing he had picked up strange Eastern religious ideas which included a belief in the transmigration of the soul – which means a spirit entering a new body after death. For another he filled the house with a pack of dogs whose company he preferred to his neighbours. He often declared he would return after death by taking over the body of his favourite spaniel.

In 1874 Major Robert Steuart died. Immediately his relatives shot his fourteen dogs, starting with the unfortunate spaniel.

The estate was left to his nephew John who moved his family into the house. Unlike his uncle he was a devout Roman Catholic, and he converted a cottage into a place of retreat for nuns. He may have been given the idea by his aunt who became a nun under the name of Sister Frances. These details were to have special importance later on.

The peculiar haunting of Ballechin House began soon after the old major's death. John Steuart's wife was at work on the household accounts in the study when she noticed a smell of dogs. It reminded her uncomfortably of when the major's pets had the run of the house. As she opened the window to let in air, she felt an invisible hound rubbing against her legs.

This experience was followed by alarming sounds for which no logical explanation could be found. Corridors echoed with knocking noises and sharp reports like the firing of guns. Sometimes there were human voices quarrelling although the actual words could not be distinguished. Towards the end of the 1870s these sounds increased and frightened the children's governess into handing in her notice.

Father Hayden, a priest who often stayed at Ballechin, said these sounds came out of the air and were sometimes so loud that he could not make himself heard. He told John Steuart that as well as the knocking, he was aware of a high-pitched scream and the noise of some creature – could it be a dog? – leaping against his bedroom door. When he flung the door open there was nothing there.

John Steuart stubbornly refused to have these happenings investigated, yet he must have been worried by them because he had an extension built for his children so they would be away from the disturbances. In January 1895 he was discussing some estate business with his agent in the late major's study when the two men were startled by three tremendous bangs. Later it was decided that these knocks must have been some sort of omen because a few days later the master of Ballechin died in a street accident while visiting London.

The estate passed to another member of the Steuart family, an army captain who had no interest in living on it. In 1896 he let the place to a wealthy family to spend the grouse-shooting season there. After they had paid a year's rent in advance they moved in – to find there was an aspect to the house which Captain Steuart had somehow forgotten to mention, namely that it was haunted.

Apart from the knockings and explosive bangs, there were now other sounds. A daughter of the family was terrified one night when she heard limping footsteps. She shouted to her brother who dashed into the room and immediately became aware that something invisible was circling her bed. What they did not know at the time was that Major Robert Steuart had returned from India with a limp, the result of a wound he had received on active service.

In September one of the guests at Ballechin wrote an account of the knockings and screams which plagued the occupants nightly, describing how doors rattled under heavy blows yet when those inside summoned up enough courage to open them there was no visible explanation. The haunting reached such a pitch that after only seven weeks' residence the family decided to leave the house and forfeit the remainder of the year's rent.

News that Ballechin House was now vacant reached the Marquis of Bute, a dedicated ghost-hunter, who seized the opportunity to investigate it. As he was unable to conduct the operation personally, he invited two famous psychic researchers, Miss Ada Goodrich-Freer and Colonel Lenesurier Taylor, to do the work for him. It proved to be one of the most remarkable investigations ever carried out in a haunted house, the results appearing in a book published in 1899 entitled *The Alleged Haunting of B— House.*

Colonel Taylor took out a lease on Ballechin House and on 3 February 1897, Miss Freer arrived to take up residence there. She was accompanied by some servants who had been hired in Edinburgh to look after a series of guests. Most of these visitors were ignorant of the house's reputation and had been selected to act as guinea pigs.

The appearance of Ballechin must have lived up to the investigators' expectations. Mantled with snow, it had an air of desolation about it and, having been unoccupied, was dreadfully cold. Miss Freer noted in her diary that on the first night her room 'was so cold that we had to cover our faces, and we had no bed linen'.

With her was Constance Moore, a daughter of Queen Victoria's chaplain, and the two shivering ladies did not have to wait long for the ghostly manifestations to begin. At three o'clock on their first morning they were aroused by banging noises in the corridor. These were followed by a menacing mutter of voices.

Miss Freer and her companions experimented with an Ouija board. This device, marked with the letters of the alphabet, uses a movable pointer to obtain messages in spiritualist seances. In answer to the question as to what the investigators could do to learn more about the hauntings, the Ouija spelled out a message telling them to go silently at dusk to a glen close to the house known as Scamp's Copse.

In the late afternoon Miss Freer followed the instructions, accompanied by two gentlemen who had been invited to Ballechin to act as independent witnesses. In her daily report she wrote: 'We went up among the trees, young firs; the snow was deep and untrodden; and when we got well off the road, we found that a burn comes down the brae side. It is frozen hard and we found it out only by the shining of the ice.

'We walked on in silence to the left of the burn, up the little valley, along a small opening between the trees and the railing which encloses them, Mr Lane-Fox first, then I, then Mr Feilding.

'In a few minutes I saw what made me stop.

'The men stopped too, and we all stood leaning over the railings, and looking in silence across the burn to the steep bank opposite. This was white with snow, except to the left, where the boughs of a large oak-tree had protected the ground.

'Against the snow I saw a slight black figure, a woman, moving slowly up the glen. She stopped, and turned and looked at me. She was dressed as a nun. Her face looked pale. I saw her hand in the folds of her habit. Then she moved on, as it seemed, on a slope too steep for walking. When she came under the tree she disappeared. . . .'

From then on the phantom of the nun was frequently seen in the glen. When new house guests arrived they were taken there as a matter of course to experience the apparition. Miss Freer described how the ghost was also seen talking to another figure and that the two spectres could be heard murmuring to each other. On 8 February 1897, she wrote: 'We went out at dusk. . . . The snow had gone, and I saw less distinctly; but I saw the nun again, and an older woman in grey, who talked earnestly with her, she answering at intervals.'

Meanwhile at the house the supernatural sounds continued – limping footsteps, thuds, the sound of someone reading monotonously, voices quarrelling and whispering and a 'detonating noise'.

The haunting of Ballechin House came to an abrupt end when a Catholic bishop and two priests said a special mass in one of the rooms. During the service Miss Freer looked from the ground floor window and saw that the figure of the nun and the other spectre had left the burn and 'come closer to the house than ever before'. She added that the nun 'looked pensive, but, as compared with last time, much relieved.'

After the service the bishop blessed the house from top to bottom, sprinkling holy water in each room and 'especially the doorway leading to the drawing-room where noises have so often been heard'.

After that Miss Freer and her fellow investigators neither saw nor heard anything unusual and, after staying for some days to be sure that the haunting was really over, left the house. In 1963 it was demolished.

Chapter 9
Midnight visitors

Ruby Bower woke at midnight with a feeling of unease.

For a moment she lay in her warm bed with her eyes closed. She knew that she was in her room at the Black Horse inn, that her uncle and aunt who ran it were nearby – yet why did she feel so strange?

She opened her eyes and the sensation of vague alarm changed to one of sheer terror. The room was bathed in an eerie light, and a rustling sound in the corner made her turn her head . . . and see a ghost!

Describing Ruby's experience, a journalist from the *Vale of White Horse Gazette* reported: '. . . her horror increased as she beheld an apparition in the shape of a stout old lady with an evil face and a grim expression, gliding slowly across the floor. Despite her fears, and the fact that the whole thing could not have lasted more than a fraction of a second, every detail of the scene is indelibly impressed on Miss Bower's memory. She recalls the old-fashioned clothes of the midnight visitor, the long fawn coloured dress of stiff silk that rustled as the old lady moved, the white apron with its frills, and the white frilly mob cap. In her hands was something which

Miss Bower was unable to distinguish.'

At this point Ruby sat up in bed and heard herself screaming, 'No! No! Don't, don't!'

At the sound of her cry the phantom disappeared by walking through the opposite wall of the room. As it vanished so did the unearthly radiance, leaving the girl trembling in the dark.

Forcing herself to be calm, Ruby climbed out of bed and went to her uncle and aunt with her story. She explained that when she awoke the room had looked different. Alterations had been carried out in it not long before, a panel being built to form a passage between the room and an outside wall in which there was a window. Yet the panel seemed to have vanished and the window appeared just as it was before the work had been done. She was so positive she had seen this extra window that, when her panic lessened, she put out her hand and was surprised to find panelling still there.

Her uncle and aunt searched the bedroom and at first there appeared to be nothing unusual about it. Then an even more mysterious aspect of the incident was discovered, when the landlord looked at a window made up of small panes of glass. On one of these the name 'John' had been scratched several times in old-fashioned handwriting.

The *Gazette* journalist wrote: 'Disbelievers would say that the writing on the window was there before Sunday – the night of the ghost's visitation – but the landlord of the hotel is confident that it was not there previously. Since he and his wife had frequently cleaned the window in question, it is inconceivable that they would not have noticed it.

'Apparently the scratches formed part of an attempt to cut a signature into the glass and, curiously enough, the scratching is obviously new – not having assumed the dark appearance common to cuts that have been made in glass for some time.'

No explanation could be found for the appearance of the signature on the window of the Cirencester inn in 1933 when Ruby Bower had her unnerving experience. As to the ghost, her relatives put forward a theory that, during some recent rebuilding of the premises, a treasure which was traditionally said to be buried there was nearly found. The spectral old lady had had to find a new hiding place.

Mr Bower told the *Gazette* that his niece was not a fanciful girl and, apart from his theory about the treasure, he could not imagine why the phantom should appear in her room.

The town was fascinated by the mystery. On 25 August – twelve days after the haunting – the local newspaper carried these headlines:

WILL THE GHOST WALK AGAIN?
SPECIAL INVESTIGATION OF
CIRENCESTER MYSTERY
COWLED FIGURES AND AN OLD CHAPEL

The story which followed said that, although no final explanation of the ghost had been reached, some light had been thrown on the mysterious phenomena by a lady medium who, being shy of publicity, was referred to as Mrs X.

The journalist described how he had gone with Mrs X – who had not seen the Black Horse before – and two of her friends into Castle Street where the hotel stands. On seeing it, Mrs X stopped dead and grasped the man by the arm.

'We are not alone,' she said. 'There are people moving all around us – people in cowls, some in brown and some in white.'

When the group entered the Black Horse Mrs X said to Ruby's aunt, Mrs Bower, 'This has all been changed. The entrance used to be through the room on the right.'

'Quite right,' answered Mrs Bower, impressed by the lady's psychic powers. 'It was altered many years ago.'

From then on Mrs X provided the sort of 'copy' that would delight any reporter. When she entered a room at the back of the building she suddenly staggered and had to cling to the doorway.

'I can't go in there,' she cried in horror. She could not explain what it was that had this effect upon her, but she had to be helped away from the room. On the first floor she remarked to Mrs Bower, 'This has been altered just here.' And again the landlady had to agree that she was right. It was obvious that in some way Mrs X was able to sense the past, and when she reached room number 3 the same feeling of horror overwhelmed her.

In the next room a dramatic change came over her and the man from the *Gazette* wrote: 'She seemed to wither, her back bowed and her left leg was twisted inwards. The fingers of her right hand were twisted and grasped some strange object. Her voice was that of an old woman. Her words came slowly. "I feel sad," she murmured, "very, very sad. I have a terrible pain in my leg. I cannot walk properly. I have a stick in my hand. I tap on the floor with it."

'Still limping, Mrs X went from room to room until she finally straightened her back and became almost "her normal self" although throughout the rest of the proceedings she was unable to straighten her leg and the foot was twisted into a grotesque position.'

The party then went up the stairs to the second floor room where Ruby had had her experience and here again Mrs X gave a demonstration of her unusual gift.

At the top of the stairs she said, 'I see a crucifix in front of me. . . .'

As the medium passed a small door leading into an attic she again said that she was unable to enter, and as she approached Ruby's room she repeated that there was a crucifix nearby. When Mrs Bower opened the door it was found that, upon a chest of drawers beside the bed, there were three crucifixes which had been placed there since the haunting.

'There is no harm meant in this room,' Mrs X told Ruby. 'You have nothing to fear in here. I cannot quite get the story clear but there was an old man and an old lady. The old lady has a long chin and a long beak-like nose. She is earthbound, she has done the old man an injury and wanders about the house. But the harm she would do or has done is not in this room. It is in one of the rooms I could not enter.'

In his *Gazette* report the journalist continued: 'The party descended the stairs to the ground floor. Then a thought struck me and I remounted the stairs examining carefully the two rooms and the attic which Mrs X had been unable to enter. The house is extremely complicated to one who does not know its geography. The stairs wind and the passages twist, and I for one found it quite impossible to know in which direction I was facing. Yet I discovered that the three rooms which had filled Mrs X with such horror *were immediately above one another*.'

On 8 September, the Black Horse was in the news again under the headline:

CIRENCESTER GHOST LAID

According to the story a lady correspondent of the newspaper received a letter from Mrs X informing her that she had received a psychic message telling her that if certain steps were taken the Black Horse ghost could be laid. At exactly three in the afternoon of the third day of the month, three white flowers should be laid in number 3 bedroom – not the room in which the ghost was seen but that one which Mrs X had been unable to enter on the first floor of the hotel.

'At about ten minutes to three on Sunday, 3 September,' the lady correspondent reported, 'Mrs X, myself, the landlord of the Black Horse and his wife, assembled in the bar parlour of the inn. We waited in silence for a few moments and then Mrs X suddenly said: "The circle is not yet complete." A little later she again spoke, remarking this time: "It's now complete. An old lady has joined us." '

Mrs X then led the way up the stairs carrying three white gladioli. This time she was able to enter number 3 bedroom and almost at once she said, 'I see two windows in front of me.' At the time the onlookers thought that this was a very strange statement for Mrs X to make because she was facing a wall, but it was later discovered that if she had been standing on the same spot years earlier she would have seen a pair of windows.

The medium laid down the three white flowers carefully, and after a brief period of silent meditation said that if the room remained locked up for three whole days the ghost would not trouble the Black Horse again.

From then on the *Vale of White Horse Gazette* never referred to hauntings at the Black Horse. But had this strange form of exorcism with the white flowers been successful? The answer is no. According to a landlord of the hotel the phantom of the old lady was seen about twenty years ago. A guest was standing in the empty bar when she looked up and saw an old woman in grey. The guest thought that she was a customer waiting to be served, but the apparition suddenly dissolved before her eyes.

Some time later a London nursing sister was on holiday at the Black Horse with her fiancé. She was staying in the haunted bedroom and he was sleeping in the room next door. During the night he was shocked into wakefulness by a scream. He raced into his girl-friend's room and found her in a state of terror. She had seen the same ghost as had awakened Ruby Bower.

Another haunted inn where an attempt was made to discover the story of its ghost by psychic means was the Bird Cage at Thame in Oxfordshire. Like the Black Horse of Cirencester, the building dates back to the fifteenth century.

Twelve years ago a Mr Neville became the manager of the quaint, timber-framed hotel and soon his wife found she was waking up during the night with a vague feeling of fear. Although it puzzled her, it did not occur to her that the cause of this unpleasant sensation could have anything to do with the supernatural.

'The first thing which convinced me that there was something uncanny here was when we had two film cameramen as guests,' Mrs Neville later explained. 'They shared a double room and after the first night one came down and said, "You've got a ghost up there." I thought he was kidding, especially when his friend said, "Don't be stupid, I slept in the same room and saw nothing." But next morning he nearly fell down stairs, all bug-eyed he was, and he said, "There *is* a blasted ghost up there."'

Mrs Neville might have got a hint as to what lay behind this when an archaeologist asked if he could inspect the Bird Cage because it was such a fascinating old building. He was particularly interested in the upper storeys which rise like a tower at one end. He told the Nevilles it was his belief that once this

70

'tower' had been used to keep lepers in.

Apart from plague, leprosy – a disease which attacks the flesh of the sufferer – was the most dreaded disease in mediaeval England. As it could be passed on by touch, lepers were greatly feared by the rest of the population. They were usually driven away from their homes and forced to ring a bell when they travelled so people could avoid them. Some old churches still have what are known as a 'leper's squint', a small hole in the wall through which the unfortunate outcasts were able to see the altar during mass.

At the Bird Cage the archaeologist found a trap-door which he thought had been used when monks or nuns – the only people who cared for lepers – passed up food in baskets on the end of long poles.

Soon afterwards Mrs Neville had an eerie experience herself. She was so intrigued by the idea the place might be haunted that late one Friday night, after cleaning up, she went to an upstairs bedroom to see if anything would happen.

'I must have dozed off,' she said, 'but suddenly I was awake. The time must have been between two-thirty and three o'clock. I remember I had a sensation of sheer terror and I leapt out of the chair thinking, "I must get downstairs!"'

'There were a lot of metal coathangers on a rail in the corner of the room and as I went to the door they clattered, just as if someone had flicked them. I thought for a moment the window must have been open and they had been moved by a breeze, but as I went through the door I hastily glanced at the window and saw it was shut tight. I felt so frightened I flew down the stairs as though the hounds of hell were after me.'

It was after this incident that the knocking started. It would begin in the early hours of the morning and continue until Mrs Neville heard the town clock strike four o'clock.

Meanwhile other people were experiencing strange happenings. An RAF officer staying at the hotel said he 'sensed a presence', adding, 'It is something I can't explain. I know it sounds crazy, but I felt there was someone else in the room with me during the night.' And one of the cameramen who had first encountered the ghost described how 'something which seemed like a cloud' whisked by his bed.

On one occasion, after Radio Oxford had broadcast a programme on the haunted inn, a customer at the bar mocked the programme and the whole idea of ghosts.

'If you don't believe, that's OK, but let's not talk about it,' said Mrs Neville. 'I believe now, although I didn't used to. . . .'

At this point a beer mug, which had been hanging on a hook, rose up and struck her painfully on the back of the neck.

'At first I thought the nail had come out,' she explained. 'I was just going to put the mug to one side when the customer went deathly pale and ran from the bar. Another man who had seen the whole thing said the mug had been lifted from the hook as though carried by an invisible hand.'

What was most upsetting for Mrs Neville was that her children began to be affected by the unseen presence. Her daughter Debbie had to be moved downstairs because she was so frightened, and on one occasion her son Chris told her that he had spent a dreadful night with the ghost 'whispering' to him.

A psychical research group had begun to visit the Bird Cage regularly in the hope of contacting the entity haunting the old inn. One of the members, Mrs Edna Weston of Watford, explained that the group had a scientific approach.

'The visit to the Bird Cage was my first contact with psychical phenomena,' she said. 'I was terrified. We went up to the room at the top of the inn and sat concentrating there until there was suddenly a furious knocking.'

She went on to describe it as terribly loud. The leader of the group questioned the spirit by asking it to knock once for 'yes' and twice for 'no'.

Gradually, through this yes-no method at their weekly sessions, the ghost-hunters began to gather information about the spirit which plagued the inn. It was the ghost of a leper who had been kept a prisoner in the room, just as the archaeologist had described earlier. But the townsfolk of Thame had not wanted anyone with the dreaded disease in their midst. They stoned him to death.

'He was very bitter and unhappy,' said Mrs Weston. 'When we suggested praying to alleviate his earthbound condition he went wild. Through his knocking he told us that he hated people, that he did not want us to disturb him and finally got the message across "Go, or I will kill you." After that there was nothing more we could do. . . .'

It was Mrs Neville who seems to have quietened the ghost. Anxious for her children, she climbed up to what was once the leper's room.

'I felt a real Charlie speaking out loud in an empty room,' she said, 'but I felt I had to do it. I said, "You are beginning to frighten my children. I don't mind you being here as long as you don't hurt any-body. . . ."' And she continued to speak like this.

'Strangely enough, the knocking stopped,' she said. 'Whether it was my words or just coincidence I don't know, but we did not hear the knocking again, although I know the ghost is still around.'

Chapter 10
Ghosts galore

'The man flew at me – and tried to kill me!' cried the youth with a shudder. These were the first words he was able to utter after he had entered a haunted room twenty minutes earlier.

The scene took place in the back wing of the Dorset manor house known as Sandford Orcas, the haunt of a frightening ghost. At full moon his wild cries have been heard echoing in the old Tudor building. In life The Screamer was a maniac kept prisoner in a room which still has an observation hole cut in its door.

The story goes that as a boy he was sent to Dartmouth College to join the Navy. While there he killed a fellow cadet and after his arrest he was found to be insane. He was sent back to Sandford Orcas where it sems that his violent fits grew worse with the waxing of the moon. During these periods he had to be restrained and the part of the house where this happened still has a sinister atmosphere about it. The legend adds that the unfortunate youth died and was buried in a hidden passage behind the Great Chamber, his family wanting to keep the facts of his madness secret.

Colonel Francis Claridge, who told the author

about the many ghosts of Sandford Orcas Manor which he was leasing, said, 'A young man who, with his girl-friend, had been round the house on several occasions, asked me if he could see a really bad room. As we entered this room I stood by the door and felt a most horrible sensation which I could not explain. Then the boy walked in and almost immediately he rushed out in a terrible state of shock and fright, and both I and his girl-friend could not get a word out of him for twenty minutes. . . . We eventually calmed him down but when he went home after an hour he was still trembling.'

Sandford Orcas must be the most haunted house in Britain with at least ten different ghosts and all kinds of strange phenomena. And it was not only Colonel Claridge and his family who experienced it. In 1967 a group of investigators from the Paraphysical Laboratory at Downton reported that 'a reasonable *prima facie* case had been made out for the hauntings', and traced manifestations experienced by people who were not members of the Claridge family over the past sixty years.

'When my wife and I took a lease on this property we were not informed it was haunted,' said Colonel Claridge. 'Since then the house has been featured on television and we have received many letters from ex-staff and others confirming many of the various apparitions.'

Mr A. W. Daniell, who had lived at the manor when he was a little boy, described how 'a very nice old lady' used to visit him when he went to bed. Two young ladies told the colonel a similar story about an old woman with a shawl appearing to them when they slept in the same bedroom. And when a BBC television team visited the house one of its members saw the phantom of a man in an old-fashioned farmer's smock.

The Sandford Orcas phantoms range from the pleasant to the sinister. One that is certainly not frightening is described as a 'dear old lady with white hair' who has been seen on the main staircase wearing a beautiful red silk dress from the Georgian period. When Colonel Claridge and his wife were searching for some lost object, they came across an old chest in the manor's priesthole. In it they found a similar red silk dress which had been put away very carefully. When they unfolded it they found that the name and the date of the death of its owner had been carefully stitched into it.

Another non-alarming spectre is that of a little dog.

'On 15 September 1972 when I was in the Great Hall, a little rough-haired fox terrier came into the room wagging his stump of a tail,' said Colonel Claridge. 'He went across the room and vanished. I then realised I had seen a ghost dog, and after making careful enquiries I found out that he died in a passage outside the Great Hall in 1900, and was the pet of a mother whose child had been born in the house. This little dog only appears on the anniversary of his death, at other times he can be heard running about in the old nursery.'

Sandford Orcas is open to the public and on one occasion two visitors turned to Mrs Claridge and asked if they should pay their entrance fee to the 'little girl in black at the foot of the stairs'. Mrs Claridge looked but could see nothing, though three weeks later she and her husband did see the apparition just as it had been described by the visitors. They said that she was dressed in a long black Victorian-style dress and appeared to be around thirteen years old.

One evening, after the last tourists had gone home, Colonel Claridge was looking over the garden when he suddenly saw a woman, rather like a gipsy in appearance, come from the gate and walk on the lawn. He was rather annoyed that she ignored him and was walking in his garden without permission. Deciding to ask her who she was and what she wanted, he stepped forward on to the lawn, but the moment his foot touched the grass the figure melted away just as the little dog had done.

A nice old lady, a Victorian child and a little dog are not the sort of ghosts to strike fear into one. But other ghosts at Sandford Orcas are far from pleasant.

One of these was the figure of a man who materialised briefly in the Claridges' bedroom for seven nights running. Each time the colonel woke to see him, he appeared to be gazing down on the four-poster bed in a menacing way. Then he would vanish.

When the week was up the ghost did not return for twelve months. Intrigued as to who he was, and using the anniversary date as a clue, Colonel Claridge read through old records until he came to the mention of a murder which had been committed long ago in Sandford Orcas at the same time of the year as the phantom's appearances. The murderer was a servant who killed his master while he was asleep in the four-poster bed by pressing a wire across his throat.

Colonel Claridge described how on several occasions he awoke to see a priest-like figure bending over the same bed. The spectre seemed to be holding a cloak as though he was about to smother somebody, but this frightening apparition did not reappear after a crucifix was attached to the bedroom door. The colonel explained it was his belief that at one time Black Magic had been practised in the manor, and the phantom priest had been connected with the Black Mass ritual. Such ceremonies might explain why there is such an extraordinary amount of supernatural activity in the house.

Another phantom – which has appeared on a photograph taken in the garden – is known as The Suicide. He was a tenant farmer who hanged himself from a pulley in the arch of the gatehouse.

The most terrifying apparition to return to Sandford Orcas is known as The Stinking Man. He makes his ghastly appearances between ten and eleven o'clock at night when he travels from the gatehouse and through the house to the staff wing where there are four bedrooms once used by servants. Here he can be heard for the rest of the night, tapping on doors. Often there is a more sinister sound, like that of a body being dragged over a floor.

Colonel Claridge said that the really horrible thing about the ghost was that when he moved through the house he left behind a smell of decaying flesh. A camera, using infra-red film, was used to photograph this phantom and showed him to be over 2 metres tall and dressed in Georgian clothes. According to research he had attacked some maid-servants.

Soon after the Claridges moved into Sandford Orcas the colonel's daughter, then aged twenty-five, decided to spend the night in the staff wing to try and discover the source of the mysterious tapping. After a while she went to sleep on a bed in one of the rooms, only to be shocked into wakefulness when she felt herself hurled to the floor. She had the sensation of fingers on her throat but, after struggling free from this invisible force, she managed to flee from that part of the house.

From then on she refused to enter the manor after nightfall.

Chapter 11
Unhappy returns

Lady Tryon's reception was in full swing at her house in London's fashionable Eaton Square. Musicians provided a pleasant background and the chatter of the guests rose higher as well-trained servants moved among them with silver trays of champagne glasses. Several people crossed to the group surrounding the hostess.

'I say, Lady Tryon, I thought your husband was away with the Mediterranean Fleet. . . .' began one.

'I beg your pardon.'

'We saw him a moment ago,' said another guest. 'Over there. I tried to speak to him, but he just passed me by. It seemed a bit odd. . . .'

'But that's ridiculous,' said Lady Tryon with a laugh. 'George is on the *Victoria*. . . .'

'Your Ladyship must be joking,' said a young woman. 'Surely he is on leave. I saw him just now in his naval uniform. . . .'

'I think it is you who must be joking,' said Lady Tryon. 'Today is June the twenty-second, not April the first, and I should know the whereabouts of my own husband. At this moment he is in command of a naval exercise off Syria. . . .'

She turned away haughtily, unaware that at that moment her husband was dying in the most extraordinary disaster in the history of the British navy.

Sir George Tryon had become Commander-in-Chief of the British Mediterranean Fleet in 1891. He seemed to be ideal for the job for it had been said 'the skilful manner in which he handled squadrons of ships extended far beyond the Royal Navy'. Two years later, at ten o'clock on the morning of 22 June, his flagship HMS *Victoria* sailed out of Beirut leading twelve ironclads.

Four hours later the ships formed two parallel columns, one of which was led by the *Victoria* and the other by HMS *Camperdown*, the flagship of Rear-Admiral Markham. Sir George ordered them to steam at a distance of 1100 metres apart. This order caused some surprise among his officers as it was usual, when ships sailed in columns, for there to be enough room for them to turn round in each other's direction without danger of collision. Eleven hundred metres did not allow for this manoeuvre and on the *Victoria* one officer asked the admiral respectfully if he really meant this distance.

Sir George retorted that he did and actually wrote down the order so there could be no mistake. The signal was sent and though the captains of the other ships were equally surprised, they obeyed immediately. After all, Sir George was regarded as the best naval commander of his day and must know what he was doing!

But did he?

At 3.15 p.m. he ordered two more signals to be made, one directing the *Victoria* to steer sixteen degrees to port and the ships following her to do likewise, while the second signal commanded the *Camperdown* to lead its column in a right-about turn.

It was obvious that if these signals were obeyed there would be a terrible series of collisions. Rear-Admiral Markham immediately questioned the order.

The *Victoria*'s signaller replied with a message from the admiral asking Markham what he was waiting for. The captains of the other ships were so obedient to their commander that all sent the reply 'Your signal is seen and understood.' Thus the course was set for disaster.

On a perfectly calm sea and in bright daylight, the *Victoria* and *Camperdown*, with coal smoke belching from their funnels, swung towards each other. On the bridge Sir George watched the manoeuvre while it became obvious to those around him that a terrifying collision was only seconds away.

Rebelling against naval discipline, Captain Bourke on the *Victoria* rang down to the engine room for full speed on one engine. He hoped this would make the *Victoria* turn in a tighter circle and thus scrape past the *Camperdown* which was now heading straight for them. On the *Camperdown* Captain Johnstone also disobeyed his admiral and gave exactly the same command to his chief engineer. Then in desperation he signalled 'Full speed astern both engines'.

But it was too late. With a horrendous grinding of metal, the *Camperdown* smashed into the starboard bow of the *Victoria*, forcing the great ship to heel over with the impact. For several minutes of utter confusion the ironclads remained locked together, then as the bow of the *Victoria* began to tilt ominously downwards the churning propellers of the *Camperdown* pulled her clear.

By now the two lines of ships, which had been about to follow the fatal manoeuvre, had managed to heave to. On their decks officers and men watched in disbelief as the *Victoria* began to settle. Orders rang out to lower boats but these were halted when the second shock of the afternoon came.

From the bridge of the stricken *Victoria* Sir George sent a signal ordering that no boats should be sent to his aid. The bewildered captains could only think that it was his intention to beach his ship in shallow water. Perhaps this was his idea because he told the helmsman to turn for the coast but, although the *Victoria*'s engines were still pounding, her rudder was out of action.

Meanwhile Captain Burke was asked by Sir George to go below to check that all watertight doors were closed, and to report on the extent of the damage. He announced that there was 'no panic, no shouting, no rushing about' as, still under the iron control of naval discipline, the seamen behaved as though they were on an exercise, not on a ship which was sinking as a result of their admiral's commands.

On the bridge Sir George remarked to his Staff Commander, 'I think she's going,' and sent another signal to the fleet, 'Have boats ready but do not send them,'

This was followed by an order to the lines of seamen on deck to 'turn about and face the sea', which they smartly obeyed. Suddenly the *Victoria* lurched to starboard, and above the noise of crashing debris in the dying ship came the voice of the ship's chaplain encouraging the crew with the song 'Steady, men, steady'.

Thirteen minutes after the collision the *Victoria* suddenly turned over and sank beneath the blue water. The last sight of her was of her propellers spinning wildly – a grim indication that her engineers and stokers had remained at their posts until the end. As the propellers hit the water again they sucked many struggling sailors to their deaths before boats from the other ships could reach them. In those last few moments 358 men were drowned, among them Sir George Tryon. Just before the *Victoria*'s final plunge he remarked to his Flag-Lieutenant who managed to swim to safety, 'It's all my fault.'

To this day the mystery of why Sir George issued those fatal orders remains, the other mystery being his appearance at his home at the moment of death.

Another point-of-death manifestation, known as the Blomberg Case, had a much happier outcome. Around the beginning of the last century in the reign of George III the wife of Edward Blomberg, a captain serving with his regiment in Martinique, died leaving behind a little boy of two years. The captain loved him dearly and was very depressed when, soon after his wife's death, he had to take dispatches to a remote part of the island. He hated the idea of leaving the child with friends, but orders were orders and he set out.

Shortly after his departure a fellow officer was awoken by a sound in his room. Opening his eyes he saw the figure of Captain Blomberg looking down through the mosquito netting draped over his bed.

'Why, Blomberg, what on earth brought you back so soon?' he asked as he struggled into a sitting position.

'This night I died,' came the low voice of the captain. 'I have come to beg you to take charge of my little boy.'

He then told the astonished officer the address of the child's grandmother in London, and asked him to send him to her as soon as possible. He also gave details of certain documents which would prove the boy's right to some property.

When he had finished, the shape of Captain Blomberg appeared to dissolve away, leaving the officer wondering whether he had dreamed the whole thing. Then he called out to a companion who shared the room with him, 'Did you see anyone come in just now?'

'Yes, it was Blomberg, wasn't it?' came the sleepy reply. 'What did he want at this time of night?'

'Did you hear what he said?'

'No. I heard him talking to you, but I couldn't make out his words.'

In the morning when the officer repeated the story in the mess there was a lot of laughter at his expense – and suggestions that he had not gone to bed sober. But that evening a message arrived at army headquarters with the news that Captain Blomberg had died of a sudden fever attack. The time of his death was identical to that which the officer claimed he had seen him.

The sequel to the story was given by the author R. H. D. Barham, who wrote: 'No time was lost in seeking out the child who was found and despatched to England, where he appears to have been somewhat coldly received by his grandmother. His story, however, happened to reach the ears of Lady Caroline Finch, the Queen's [Queen Charlotte] governess, who repeated it to Her Majesty. The Queen, struck by the interest attached to the boy, declared that little Blomberg should never want for a home; and immediately sending for him ordered that he should be brought up in the Royal nursery. She afterwards provided for his education and saw to the settlement of his property. In addition to this, when the lad reached the age of nine years, the Queen employed Gainsborough to paint his portrait, and subsequently presented the picture to the original. This lad, brought up at the palace, became in due time chaplain to George IV.'

Chapter 12
The Scrap Faggot

'Look at that thing in the fireplace!' cried the girl. Then her eyes rolled upwards and she slumped to the floor in a faint. Her friend knelt beside her, cradling her head and murmuring, 'Carol, Carol, what did you see?'

In the bar of the pub a few of the regulars gazed at the fireplace but it appeared perfectly normal.

'She's coming round,' someone said as the girl on the floor opened her eyes.

'What did you see, Carol?' repeated her friend.

Carol gave a shudder.

'It was a shape . . . a shape that was like a human figure,' she said. 'It was standing in the fireplace beneath the chimney, and it was evil! I'm never coming here again!'

And Carol never did return to the St Anne's Castle Inn at Great Leighs in Essex. She was not the only one to be scared away from the haunted pub.

'A drayman came from the Romford brewery which supplies our beer,' said the landlord Dennis Higginson. 'I left him alone in the cellar putting the beer out. When I returned he had jumped out of the cellar and stood shaking by his dray. "I'm never going into your cellar again," he said. "Don't be stupid, Jock," I said. "Come on, now." "Not likely," he answered. "Not after that thing was standing behind me." And since then Jock refuses to come on this round.'

The restless *thing* which haunts the St Anne's Castle, and other parts of the village, is the ghost of a witch. That such a ghost should appear in Essex is not so surprising as it has been called the Witch County.

It was during the reign of Queen Elizabeth that the authorities became worried about witchcraft and made harsh laws against witches. This came about because attempts had been made to assassinate the queen by use of magic and, though the idea may seem far-fetched to us today, the threat appeared real enough to the Elizabethans. In 1563 the Witchcraft Act was passed which was to bring terror to people accused of having pacts with the Devil and practising Black Magic.

The Act led to the execution of many hundreds of so-called witches and, although torture was not legal in England for witch trials, the methods of interrogation were so ruthless they seemed very close to torture. But in one respect the new laws were merciful. When a witch had been sentenced to death – not for practising magic but for committing crimes by means of witchcraft – the penalty was carried out by hanging and not, as in Scotland and on the Continent, by burning at the stake. The last official witchcraft execution in Britain took place in 1727 when Janet Horne was burned alive in Scotland.

In Essex the first trials were held after the passing of the Witchcraft Act when three women were brought to court at Chelmsford. Elizabeth Francis was imprisoned for putting a spell on a child so that it became weak-minded and Agnes Waterhouse was hanged after being found guilty of sending an imp, in the shape of a cat, to kill a cow and geese belonging to a neighbour she disliked. Her daughter, who had been accused of having a 'familiar' in the form of a toad, was allowed to go free.

In 1582 thirteen more women were tried at Chelmsford, two of whom were hanged. One of these was Elizabeth Bennet who said she caused the death of a neighbour named William Byett and his wife by sending two imps named Lierd and Suckin after them. The odd thing was that while many innocent people – often old ladies who lived alone and kept pets to whom they talked for company – were found guilty of witchcraft, a surprising number of suspects boasted of their supernatural powers.

In the seventeenth century Essex, and the whole of East Anglia, became the hunting ground of Matthew Hopkins of Manningtree. Known as The Witch-finder General, he travelled from town to town to seek out witches and have them tried, being paid a fee for each one who was found guilty. In one day alone, nineteen of his victims were hanged.

Even members of the clergy could not escape. A seventy-year-old parson, who was rather unpopular with his congregation at Brandeston in Suffolk, was accused of witchcraft. The poor old man was forced to walk up and down a room between Witch-finder General and his assistant until he collapsed and confessed to sending a demon to sea to sink a ship.

Sentenced to hang, he was not even allowed the spiritual support of a fellow vicar, with the result that he conducted his own funeral service before the execution.

With such witch-hunting going on it is not surprising that the ghosts of some victims should linger on. So it was in Great Leighs.

A witch was executed in the village and her body,

with a stake through her heart, was buried in a small triangle of turf where three roads made a Y-junction close to the St Anne's Castle Inn. This was in keeping with the old belief that witches should be buried in unhallowed ground at a crossroads. To make doubly sure that the witch would not trouble them, the villagers rolled a large boulder over her grave. From that day to this the grass triangle has been known as Scrap Faggot Green – Scrap Faggot being the old Essex name for a witch.

The years rolled by and all that was remembered of the witch was a vague legend and the stone in the centre of the green. Then came the Second World War when American bases were established in Essex. Huge military trucks roared through Great Leighs but when they came to the Y-junction at Scrap Faggot Green they had great difficulty in getting round it because of their size. The US Army was not going to let a witch's gravestone get in the way of winning the war. A bulldozer was brought up and the boulder pushed out of the way so that the trucks could drive over the grass.

From then on peculiar things began to happen in the village. Some were frightening and some were comical. Mr Higginson, of the St Anne's Castle Inn, said: 'One farmer had quite a few hens and another chap up the road had a lot of ducks. When they got up one morning the chap who owned the hens found he had the ducks, while the duck owner had all the hens. You might say it was the work of an ordinary practical joker, but have you ever tried to catch dozens of ducks at night without making any noise?'

Whether this was a supernatural joke or not, tampering with livestock was the sort of thing blamed on witches in Essex!

It seems that the spirit of the witch, after being released by the removal of the stone, plagued the villagers for a while and then took up residence in the St Anne's Castle Inn.

'Strange things have happened here,' the landlord said. 'One Sunday night my son and I were watching an Eamonn Andrews show on television and my wife put out supper on the table and said, "I'll have a bath while you have your food and watch the show."

'We ate the meal and did not move from the room. Then my wife came down in her dressing gown and said, "You both knew I was in the bathroom so why did you keep trying to open the door and rattling the handle?" We told her that we hadn't been out of the room, but she swore that someone had walked along the corridor and had tried to force the door. But no one else was in the building and the dogs were with us, so it was not one of them pressing against the door.'

Another pub to have a haunting connected with witchcraft is the Wellington Hotel at the village of Riding Mill in Northumberland. In this case the ghost is not a witch but a victim of the witches who used to meet at the building when it was a private house.

Not long ago alterations were carried out at the Wellington and an old kitchen was found which had been sealed off. It is now an extension to the bar known as The Little Back Room. Here the witches of Riding Mill used to hold their ceremonies, and it is to this room that the phantom of Anne Armstrong is believed to return.

The name Anne Armstrong is well known to those who study the history of witchcraft because of the astonishing evidence she gave in the great Northumbrian Witch Trial of 1673.

The case began when Anne had an argument with an old market woman over some eggs. Anne won the petty argument but later she became convinced that the old woman had given her the 'evil eye'. This feeling of being hexed was followed by a meeting with a stranger in ragged clothes who warned Anne that if she turned to the Witches' God she would be trapped forever. He added that if she wanted to escape the clutches of the local witches she must never accept any food from them.

Anne was upset by this mysterious warning. Who was the ragged man? And why should witches be interested in her? She became more worried when she began to go into trances. When she awoke from them she babbled extraordinary stories about witches and how they ill-treated her.

These accounts can still be read because, on 5 February 1672, she became so terrified over what was happening to her that she went before the Newcastle magistrates and charged several women with witchcraft.

In the statement she named a woman, Ann Forster, who she said 'came with a bridle and bridled her, changed her into a horse and rode upon her till they came to the rest of her companions at Riding Mill Bridge End, where they usually met.' Here the witches enjoyed themselves singing and dancing.

'At the same time,' Anne testified, 'they were constantly changing shape.' This shape-changing continued until the bewitched victim was ridden home again.

Anne also described how a rope hung from the ceiling of what is now The Little Back Room to provide food for the witches' feasts. She said under oath: 'By swinging on a rope tied to the rafter whereupon all manner of things were set upon the table – broth, chickens, cheese, mutton and bottles of sac.'

The accused women were brought for trial the following year and Anne told the court how the witches 'danced with their devils', and one of them named Anne Baites had a demon whom she called her 'Protector' – an odd name because he would beat her when she was slow to do his bidding.

Anne also described the magic rope to the court in words still to be found on an old document: '. . . their protector [the Devil] which they called their god, sitting at the head of the table in a gold chaire, as she thought; and a rope hanging over the roome which everyone touched three several times and whatever was desired was sett upon the table . . . of several kindes of meat and drink, and when they were eaten, she that was last drew the table and kept the revision. Ann Forster did swing upon the rope and upon the first swing she gott a cheese and upon the second she gott a beatment of wheatflower and upon the third swing she gott about half a quarter of butter, to kneed the flour withall, they having noe power to gett water.'

Unfortunately the records of the trial are incomplete and we do not know the fate of the Riding Mill witches. There are no records of them being executed and they probably went free. It could be that Anne Armstrong's story was too fantastic for even those who believed utterly in the power of witchcraft.

According to old legends the witches sought revenge for being taken to court, somehow luring Anne Armstrong back to the room where they had their meetings. Here they hanged her from the very rope that she had told the magistrates was used to provide food and drink. Little wonder the room was sealed up, and for three centuries the villagers have believed that the ghost of Anne Armstrong periodically revisits the scene of her murder.

Chapter 13
Who goes there?

'Who goes there?'

The challenge rang through the hall of Hinton Ampner Manor.

'Luttrell, what's happened?' cried Captain Jervis, running into the hall in his night-shirt. At the far end by an open doorway stood his friend Captain Luttrell, a lamp held high.

'It was those damn' noises again,' exclaimed Luttrell. 'I heard someone across the floor here, but when I opened the door . . . nothing!'

For a moment the two men looked about them in uneasy silence. The manor was quiet, unusually quiet which in a way made it more sinister. To the two naval men it was as though the house was waiting for something to happen.

'Look – against the door!' shouted Jervis.

Luttrell spun round, white-faced.

'Something flitted past me,' explained the other. 'Ah, those sounds again. . . .'

Both men listened. It seemed that an invisible person was walking in the hall. This was followed by a snatch of music, then a low murmuring sound which filled the air about them.

'This time I'm going to get to the bottom of this, Jervis,' Luttrell declared. 'Help me search the house.'

The friends went from room to room, from cellar to attic, until dawn light began to filter through the windows, but they found nothing to explain the strange sounds which seemed to be mocking them.

'There's only one thing for it,' said Jervis as the two men parted to snatch some sleep. 'My sister must leave this accursed house.'

'I fear for her safety if she remains,' said Captain Luttrell gravely. 'There is something in this place which reeks of evil.'

The manor house at Hinton Ampner, in Hampshire, had been built in the sixteenth century, and it came into the possession of Lord and Lady Stawell in 1719 through an inheritance. Twenty-one years later Lady Stawell died and, according to the gossip of the time, an 'attachment' grew between Lord Stawell and his late wife's sister Honoria, who also lived at Hinton Ampner. They were unable to get married because the law would not allow a man to marry his sister-in-law.

Rumours spread that a baby had been born to Honoria but that it had been secretly done away with to avoid scandal. Whatever the truth, it would seem that something terrible must have happened at the old manor house to cause the manifestations which followed.

In 1754 Honoria died and was soon followed by Lord Stawell, and then came Hinton Ampner's first sign of being haunted. A groom of the house swore that he had seen the phantom of his late master 'drably dressed'. At the time not much notice was taken of his story, but it was to be remembered later.

The house stood empty for ten years and then it

was let to a family by the name of Ricketts. Mr Ricketts, a successful merchant, went on a long visit to the West Indies soon after he and his wife Mary had settled in with their children.

It was as though the ghosts of Hinton Ampner had been waiting for someone to haunt. On the arrival of the family doors opened and slammed by themselves even after new locks had been fitted, a nursemaid had hysterics when she saw the ghost of a 'gentleman in drab clothes', other servants glimpsed a female ghost and heard the rustle of a silk dress while 'dismal groans' filled the corridors at night.

The haunting of Hinton Ampner was precisely described by Mary Ricketts in letters to her husband, brother and the rector of the village. She found the ghostly manifestations so remarkable that she also wrote a 'Narration' on them to be kept by her family, and which was published just over a hundred years ago by *The Gentleman's Magazine*.

'Some time after Mr Ricketts left me, I, then sleeping in the bedroom over the kitchen, frequently heard the noise of someone walking in the room within,' she wrote. 'Although we often made instant search, we never could discover any appearance of human or brute being. . . .' It is possible to trace in her Narration how from then on the supernatural phenomena increased and new forms of haunting began.

'I once or twice heard sounds of music and one night in particular three distinct and violent knocks as though someone was beating with a club or other heavy weapon against the door downstairs,' Mary recorded. 'I thought that house-breake.s must be forcing their way in and immediately rang my bell. No one answered it, but as the noise ceased I thought no further of it at the time. After this, and in the beginning of the year 1771, I was frequently conscious of a hollow murmuring which seemed to fill the whole house. It was like no other sound that I have heard, and could not have been caused by the wind, as it occurred on the calmest nights.'

This menacing murmur continued through the following months and, along with other disturbances, reached a peak by the middle of the year. A new aspect of the haunting was the sounds of people – a woman and two men – talking together in low voices. Mary Ricketts was unable to distinguish the actual words, but the horrible thing about these conversations was that they always ended in a scream which died away slowly.

It was then that Mary's brother Captain Jervis came to stay at Hinton Ampner and her account of the happenings was backed up by Captain Luttrell, a friend and neighbour. The two men decided to investigate the disturbances for themselves, and this began with Luttrell sitting up all night and hearing the phantom footsteps.

'My brother sat up every night during the week he spent at Hinton Ampner,' Mary wrote. 'In the middle of one of them I was alarmed by the sound of a gun or pistol, discharged quite close to me, and immediately followed by groans as of a person in agony or on the point of death. . . . My brother now earnestly begged me to leave the house.'

She took his advice, moving her family to London in August 1771. The manor house, now the talk of the neighbourhood, remained empty for a year and was then let to a family named Lawrence. As with the Ricketts, strange things began to happen as soon as they moved in. Soon afterwards they left hurriedly.

After that Lady Hillsborough, who owned the ill-omened manor, could not get a tenant to stay there. It was shunned by everybody, and left alone to its ghosts it gradually became derelict. Finally Lady

Hillsborough ordered it to be demolished and a new house was built in the grounds to replace it.

Such is the story of Hinton Ampner. But there is a postscript. As workmen doing the demolition work tore up some floorboards they found 'a small skull said to be that of a monkey'. There was no explanation of how such an unusual object might have got there. Was it perhaps the skull of a murdered baby?

Another ghost to be challenged by a naval captain was the Brown Lady of Raynham Hall. Captain Marryat was the author of such books as *Mr Midshipman Easy* which used to be very popular with schoolboys. On this occasion he was the guest of Lord Townshend who owned the seventeenth-century house known as Raynham Hall, at East Raynham in Norfolk. Being interested in the supernatural, the captain arranged to sleep in the bedroom reputed to be haunted by the Brown Lady, and in which hung a portrait showing her in a brown brocade dress.

He was just about to go to bed when Lord Townshend's two young nephews came to discuss a gun which was to be used in a shooting party the next morning. The captain said he would be interested to see it and he went with them to their room. A few minutes later they accompanied him back along the corridor, joking that they would protect him from the Brown Lady.

Suddenly their laughter was silenced as they saw a female figure advancing towards them. As she came nearer Captain Marryat realised he had seen her before – she was the subject of the portrait in his bedroom. She held a lamp which showed that her dress was made of brown brocade, and as she passed the three men she glanced at them 'in such a diabolical manner' that their blood was chilled.

At that moment the captain raised the gun and fired.

Not being the sort of man to shoot fellow house guests, he must have been sure that it was not a living person he was aiming at when he pulled the trigger. And his target was certainly not of this world. The bullet went right through her and was later found embedded in a door.

The Brown Lady had been Dorothy Walpole, the daughter of Robert Walpole, the MP for Houghton in Norfolk, and the sister of the famous Sir Robert Walpole. Her father was the guardian of Viscount Charles Townshend with whom she fell madly in love, but when the young couple asked for permission to marry the old man refused. He was afraid that it would appear that he was scheming if he married his daughter to his wealthy ward.

Lord Townshend married someone else but when she died in 1711 he married his first love.

At the time he did not know that during his first marriage Dorothy had been admired by the notorious Lord Wharton whose unpaid gambling debts forced him to flee England. When Lord Townshend discovered that Dorothy had returned his feelings he was furious. How could the woman he had taken as his wife have cared for a scoundrel like Wharton?

Forgetting that he had turned to someone else when Dorothy's father had not allowed them to wed, he accused poor Dorothy of being unfaithful to him. In revenge he kept her locked in her apartments at Raynham Hall where she died of smallpox in 1726. Some said it was a broken heart rather than disease which ended her life, and one grim legend states that she was found with a broken neck at the foot of the grand staircase.

It is thought that her spirit returns to the house in search of the children her harsh husband parted her from.

One of the Brown Lady's most famous appearances was recorded in 1849. A guest named Major Loftus had played a long game of chess with a friend and was about to go to his bedroom when the other man pointed to the figure of a woman standing at the door. The men were surprised because she was dressed in a costume which would have been fashionable a century earlier. While they stared at her she gradually dissolved.

The next night the major saw her again. This time he met her face to face and declared afterwards that the horrible thing about the ghost was its empty eye sockets.

Eighty-five years later the Brown Lady was still haunting Raynham Hall, which was proved by a remarkable photograph which appeared in the 1936 Christmas issue of *Country Life*. It had been taken for the magazine by Captain Provand. With his assistant Mr Indre Shira, he had been asked to do an illustrated feature on the house which has been described as one of the best of its date in Norfolk.

The photographers had set up their equipment opposite the staircase when Mr Shira shouted that he could see an apparition and asked Captain Provand to release the shutter. The captain did so, though he said that he could see nothing unusual in the viewfinder.

'I'll bet you five pounds that there'll be an impression of a woman on the plate,' said Mr Shira. And he won his bet. The negative, which shows the Brown Lady, was examined by experts who were unable to find any hint of faking.

Chapter 14
Murder mystery

John Dunkerly was a Peeping Tom, one of those strange people who get pleasure out of spying on others. But when he crept up on Tom Otter and his wife he got more than he bargained for. Not only did he witness a murder – he became haunted!

The drama began on 3 November 1805, when Dunkerly left The Sun Inn which stands on the bank of the Fossdyke canal at Saxilby in Lincolnshire. Night was falling as he set out for his home village of Doddington. Near a place known as Drisney Nook he met three friends who called as they passed, 'You'll have company on the road, John.'

They were referring to a man named Thomas Otter who had got married that day, a man feared because of his foul temper and who was always quarrelling with the girl who had just become his wife.

Before long Dunkerly caught sight of the couple as they walked along the moonlit lane.

'Sit down, you can rest here,' he heard Tom Otter growl. Grinning at this chance to spy on them, Dunkerly went into a field and sneaked along a hedge until he was close to where Mrs Otter sat alone on a bank. With a chill of fear he saw that Tom Otter had climbed into the hedge a few yards away. But the bridegroom did not notice the Peeping Tom, he was too busy pulling up a stake.

'The moon shined on his face at the time and his eyes frightened me,' Dunkerly said in evidence later. 'There was such a fiery look in them, like a cat's eyes in the dark, and I heard him say to himself, "That'll finish my wedding!" Then he climbed down to where she was sitting with her head hanging down, and he swung the hedgestake with both hands and hit her a clout on the head. She gave one scream and called on God for mercy, then tumbled over with her head on the ground. He hit her again as she lay on the grass, and that time the knock sounded as though he had hit a turnip. I saw her arms and legs all of a-quiver like for a while and then she was as still as a cobble-stone. I think I went off in a faint.

'When I came round again, the hedgestake he had murdered her with lay close beside me. I took it up and my hand was covered with red, and my smock sleeve dabbled with it. Then I thought if they found me in that state they'd take me for the murderer and hang me, so for days I wandered about. I don't know how long, working on roads and getting a job as how I could.'

Meanwhile Tom Otter had been arrested at The Sun when an alert constable noticed a bloodstain on his clothes. And it was to The Sun that his wife's body was brought for the inquest. Blood dripped from it as it was carried over the threshold and the inn servants were ordered to clean it up. Superstitiously they refused, declaring they would rather be fired than touch the blood of a murder victim. Four months later the stains were still to be seen on the floor.

Found guilty of murder, Tom Otter was sentenced

to be executed at Lincoln. Afterwards his body was taken to be hung in irons from a gibbet at the scene of the crime as an example to other violent persons.

Country folk watched fearfully from the fields as the black waggon carrying the corpse creaked down the lanes. At Saxilby a curious crowd came out of The Sun as it crossed the bridge. The spectators streamed after it, eager to reach Drisney Nook where Otter's body would be exhibited until it was no more than a skeleton within an iron frame.

Just as the cart reached the other side of the canal, the bridge collapsed and twenty people were plunged into the water. Everyone was convinced that the malice of the dead murderer had inspired the accident and soon there was another example of it.

After the Saxilby blacksmith had riveted the body into its irons, it was attached to a rope and hoisted beneath the arm of the gibbet by a team of men. As it dangled above them the beam snapped and its gruesome burden plummeted on top of them.

The gibbet was repaired and the body hauled into place for the second time.

'Well, he won't come down again!' remarked John Dunkerly with satisfaction. At that moment the remains of Tom Otter did come down again, flattening the Peeping Tom.

At Saxilby the landlord of The Sun had a keen eye for business. Somehow he acquired the stake which Otter had used to kill his wife, and now he exhibited it in the bar of the inn.

'It might have been unlucky for Mrs Otter,' he joked as he watched extra customers crowding in to drink ale and gape at the bloodstained relic. 'But her misfortune has been my good luck. There ain't nothing that folks enjoy more than a good murder and that stake is a right good investment.'

Then something very strange happened.

On the anniversary of the killing the stake vanished from its place behind the bar, and several days later a farmer walked in carrying it.

'I found this here at Drisney Nook,' he said laying it on the bar. 'It were right by the spot where that poor girl were done in by Tom Otter last year. I reckoned it might be worth a pint or two if I took the trouble to bring it back.'

On the next anniversary of Mrs Otter's death the stake vanished again, and no one was all that surprised when it turned up at Drisney Nook. Now there was no talk of thieves or practical jokers, the opinion of the Saxilby folk was that it was a supernatural power which transported the stake back to the fatal spot.

The landlord was of the same opinion and no longer wanted the sinister souvenir in his bar. He gave it to a friend who ran an inn at Torksey and who was prepared to brave the stake's uncanny reputation in order to boost his business. So his more unruly customers would not interfere with it, he had it fastened to the wall. But when 3 November came the stake was torn from its fastenings by an unknown force. In the morning its owner went straight to Drisney Nook where it was lying by a hedge.

Returning home, he looked for a long time at the broken hasps hanging from the wall – and decided the extra business was not worth it. The stake still had value as a bar-room attraction and he sold it to the landlord of the Peewit Inn. The new owner was determined to end its disappearances and paid the Saxilby blacksmith to make cast iron staples to secure it. But on the next anniversary of the murder these vanished along with the exhibit.

At least there was no trouble in finding it. Yet again it was lying by a hedge at Drisney Nook. Back in the Peewit Inn it was bolted to the wall.

The following November a party of villagers planned to stay the night in the inn and see what happened when the time came for the stake to keep its uncanny appointment. Having fortified themselves with brandy, they settled down to keep watch in the darkened bar. But they must have over-fortified themselves because every one nodded off to sleep. When they opened their bleary eyes the morning light showed that the clamps had been wrenched from the wall and the weapon spirited away.

The activities of the hedgestake had now become too alarming for the locals. They feared it was the Devil's work and to calm them the Bishop of Lincoln ordered it to be burned beneath the walls of Lincoln cathedral.

As far as the public were concerned this was the end of the puzzling affair but, during his last illness, John Dunkerly told a clergyman how the stake returned to Drisney Nook. The vicar passed the extraordinary account on to a well-known author who made it public.

'It was the very night of the murder, exactly a twelve-month afterwards, that I felt doley-like [depressed], so I went to bed about dusk hours, and what I'm trying to tell you is as true as I'm a dying man,' Dunkerly confessed. 'I couldn't sleep, and while I was like that, all of a sudden Tom Otter stood in front of me in his chains, and says: "It's time, come along." And I had to go with him. And he says: "Fetch it – make haste." And I broke into The Sun, at Saxilby, and fetched the hedgestake that he had murdered her with from off the nail where it was hanging up, and when I got outside the door they were both waiting for me, and we all three went over Saxilby bridge together.

'She was walking behind and carrying a paper box in one hand and a pair of pattens [these were overshoes for keeping shoes out of the mud] in the other. She was wearing the light blue gown she had on that very night the year before. He had on the same light velveteen jacket and breeches that he had on when he came through the hedge and tore up the stake that I was carrying then.

'It was a kind of mist we seemed to be walking in. We turned down Drisney Nook Lane, and reached the spot we reached before, and he used the very same words, and said: "Sit down. You can rest here." And she sat down with her head drooping on her breast, like before, and he came up to me, with his eyes more fiery than they was before-time, and says: "Now then, quick."

'And somehow I threw up the hedgestake with both hands and murdered her just the way he did twelve months before. I give her one clout when she was sitting down, and another when she'd fallen over. And every third of November for years, no matter where I might be, the same low-doley feeling came over me, and Tom Otter would come to me in his chains and say: "Now then, it's time," and I had to go and fetch the hedgestake from wherever it might be, and do the same murdering over again, and twice when it was fastened up with staples he came and helped me pull, and said: "You pulled hard enough when you helped to gibbet me!"

'The hedgestake was always found in the stubble field next morning where I'd thrown it like he did, and when I'd find myself walking back home I'd be all wet with sweat.

'I had no peace until that stake was burnt in the Minster yard. After that was done they never came to fetch me to go with them to murder her no more.'

Chapter 15
The Holy Trinity phantoms

'There! There!'

A hushed whisper rippled through the church and the eyes of the congregation swivelled away from the preacher to the church's east windows. Beyond one of them something was seen to be moving – the graceful figure of a young woman walking with a light step. She passed out of sight and seconds later was seen opposite the second window. She was entirely covered with a fine lace veil which showed the outline of her head. A moment later she vanished.

The congregation settled back to wait. They knew they had just seen a phantom and in a little while they would glimpse her again.

'In two or three minutes the figure returned,' an eyewitness wrote later, 'the robe flowing back in the same way, and disappeared behind the organ window. . . .'

The haunting of Holy Trinity Church, at Micklegate in York, was so regular that many people swelled the Sunday congregation in the hope of seeing the figure. Often they were not disappointed, as we see from a report which appeared in *The Chronicle* of 6 May 1876. A correspondent with the initials

H.G.F.T. wrote: 'On Good Friday last I went to Holy Trinity Church, York, for morning service, at 11 o'clock, and repaired with a friend to the gallery, being anxious to see a certain apparition which is said to haunt the place.

'The gallery is situated at the extreme west end of the building, and faces the east window, from which it is distant some 18 metres or so. The gallery was full and though many of them afterwards said they saw it, they were not in the least affected by the apparition, treating it as a matter of course, to which they were well accustomed.'

The writer continued that although he watched the east window during the long service – and although others claimed to have seen something – he noticed nothing abnormal and left the church believing himself to be the victim of a hoax. But so many of his friends assured him they saw the phenomenon every Sunday, he decided to try once more.

He went to an Easter Day service and half-way through it his eyes 'which had hardly once moved from the left or north side of the window, were attracted by a bright light formed like a female robed and hooded passing from north to south with a rapid gliding motion outside the Church, apparently at some distance'.

H.G.F.T. went on to describe the apparition as being transparent 'yet thick (if such a term can be used) with light. It did not resemble linen, for instance, but was far brighter and would no doubt have been dazzling to a new observer.'

When the figure passed out of sight, a friend whispered to him it would return. It did so in five minutes, gliding back the way it had come.

Half an hour later the phantom appeared yet again, passing from north to south, outside the Gothic window. It returned accompanied by the figure of a young child, then vanished in front of the last pane but one in the window.

'I did not see the child again, but a few seconds afterwards the woman reappeared, and completed the passage, behind the last pane, very rapidly,' the correspondent continued. 'Nothing more was seen during the service ... any figure required to be produced by reflection on the east window would have to be standing or walking in the centre of the aisle.

'For the above facts I can vouch, and I have no reason to believe that the following are either incorrect or exaggerated. It is said to appear very frequently on Trinity Sunday, and to bring two other figures on to the scene, another female, called the nurse, and the child. It is often seen as distinctly on a dark, rainy, or snowy day, and when the sun is shining. When I saw it the sun was not bright.

'The motion is even, not at all jerky. Sometimes it glides swiftly; at other times slowly. It cannot be a mere accidental reflection, from a door or a window, for instance, for the figure faces different ways, according to the direction in which it is going; and it is not always alone, nor do the figures always act in consort.

'One of my friends, with a companion, has watched outside on the wall, where he had a full view of the whole place around, during morning service. The ghost has been seen from the inside, while outside nothing was visible.'

The explanation for the ghosts went back to an outbreak of plague in York two centuries earlier. Then a child and her nursemaid died of the disease and were buried outside the city walls in a plague pit. The child's mother survived the pestilence, and when she died she was buried normally in the Holy Trinity churchyard. Here her spirit returned to wait for the phantom nursemaid to bring her daughter to her for a tragically brief reunion before parting until, in some mysterious way, the scene was acted out again.

In 1951 a local schoolteacher was showing a friend who was a keen historian round the ancient churches of York. It was evening when the two ladies reached Holy Trinity and while her friend explored the building, the teacher went to the west end of the church and loitered at the spot where H.G.F.T. sat eighty-one years earlier. Suddenly the temperature about her dropped alarmingly and her surroundings changed to what she described as 'earthy and cold, a very charnel house atmosphere of death and decay'.

She did not attribute her sensations to a supernatural source until seven years later, when she heard of the church's haunted history.

If you visit York's Holy Trinity Church today you will see a notice at the gate stating that the church was the site of a haunting.

There are over a hundred-and-fifty haunted churches in Britain, and some of them have very strange stories. Take, for example, the phantom bird which haunted West Drayton Church in Middlesex for over a century. . . .

Late one winter's night in 1749 three men were hurrying past the black bulk of the church when they heard shrill screams, so high-pitched that they sounded non-human.

'I've never heard anything like this, it fair chills the blood,' said one of the men, pausing. 'Murder's being done and no mistake.'

'There's something uncanny about this church,' one of his friends muttered. 'Have you heard tell about the knocking sounds that come out of it on Friday nights? They do say it's because a victim of murder and the man that killed him were buried in the same vault. . . .'

The third man held up his lantern and looked about him.

'At least those are not knocking sounds,' he declared. 'Some poor soul's in trouble. Let's see what we can do to help.'

With many a glance over their shoulders, the trio began to look for the source of the shrieks which still echoed at intervals. After a few minutes the man carrying the lamp said, 'It seems to come from that vault. . . .'

'Then it must be a spook,' said one of his companions. 'Let's get away from here, it's dangerous interfering with the Dead.'

The light from the lantern was now playing on a grating set in the wall and, despite their fears, the searchers craned forward to see what might be revealed. A moment later they leapt back in surprise.

A huge black bird had hurled itself against the iron grille, flapping its wings furiously while its cries echoed through the foggy night.

'It looks like a raven,' said one of the men after they had laughed at their needless fear. 'The poor creature must have got trapped in there.'

'I don't see how it could have got in,' said the lantern-carrier. 'It's too big to have squeezed between those iron bars. Let's get it set free tomorrow.'

Still chuckling at their adventure, the men went home but when they reported it to the parish clerk the next day they found it was not so straightforward as they had imagined.

'That was no ordinary bird you saw in the vault,' they were told. 'That's the ghost bird.'

Smiling at their astonishment, the parish clerk added that he had seen it himself, sometimes in the vaults and sometimes in the chancel of the church.

'How do you know it's a ghost?' one asked.

'Because it fades away like a ghost. And don't think I'm imagining it. My wife and daughter have seen it happen, too.'

Not long after this incident a young man entered the church and saw a very large black bird perched near the altar. It seemed to be real enough, and he decided that it must be this creature which had given rise to the stories about the church being haunted. If he could only catch it!

It would be hard to seize it by himself, so he hastily went to some bell ringers and asked them to help him in the hunt. They picked up pieces of wood as clubs and rushed into the main part of the church. The alarmed bird fluttered along the aisle and in between some pews. One of the ringers hit it so hard with his baton that it landed screaming in a corner.

With a shout of triumph the men dived forward with outstretched hands to grab the furious bundle of feathers, but before they could close on the bird it seemed to melt away.

The ghost bird was reported many times after this, usually in the vaults or perched on the rail in front of the altar. Its last appearance was seen by two ladies who were startled by it when they were arranging flowers in the church one day in 1869 – a hundred and twenty years after it had first been seen.

In 1883 the Reverend F. G. Lee, a well-known author on ghostly topics, wrote about the bird after the wife of a rector at the church had informed him of its history, adding that she often heard mysterious fluttering sounds when she was in the church. And a certain Mrs White, who lived in the West Drayton parish, told him that 'the country folk always believed that the Spectral Bird which haunted Drayton Church was the restless and miserable spirit of a murderer who had committed suicide and who, through family influence, instead of being put into a pit or hole with a stake through his body at the crossroad at Harmondsworth, as was the sentence by law, had been buried in consecrated ground'.

For over two centuries the people of Renwick in Cumbria have been referred to as 'Bats'. The puzzle as to why they should have this odd nickname is solved if you visit the village church of All Saints which has a document with the intriguing title 'Why the Inhabitants of the Village are called Renwick Bats'.

The story it tells goes back to 1733 when a number of workmen were employed to demolish the old church to make way for a new one. Most of the walls had been reduced to rubble when one of the men suddenly gave a scream. From a yawning gap in the foundations there appeared a huge winged shape, a terrifying black *thing* which swooped through the dust of demolition towards those who had disturbed it.

The men fled and the villagers barred their doors and windows as the creature's evil shadow passed over their homes.

The flapping horror was recognised as a Cockatrice, a fantastical beast which in the Middle Ages was believed in along with dragons and griffins. It was said to be a four-legged cock with huge thorny wings and a serpent's tail which ended in a hook. According to Chaucer its gaze could strike people dead. It is strange that such a name should be used to describe this mysterious creature in the eighteenth century.

Not all the villagers remained paralysed with fear. One by the name of John Tallantire armed himself with a branch from a rowan tree – often known as the

Witch Tree because of its magical properties – and attacked the Cockatrice in the churchyard. John's strength, coupled with the power of the rowan wood, proved too much for the monster which was finally killed close to the ruins where it had been disturbed.

John Tallantire was hailed as a hero, and the account in the village church says: 'For this act his estate was enfranchised (made over without debt) to him and his heirs forever.' And he was also excused from paying church taxes.

The description of the creature as an actual Cockatrice must have been an exaggeration at the time, but whatever it was did have a batlike shape and from then on the locals were nicknamed 'Renwick Bats'.

And the original Renwick 'bat' seems to linger on in a phantom form. The author Gerald Findler wrote in his *Ghosts of the Lake Counties*, published in 1972: '. . . records show that since then, even as recently as ten years ago, people say they have seen an enormous black bird-like figure flying around Renwick on certain evenings.'

In the Church of St James, which stands in Garlick Hill in the City of London, an American boy gazed with morbid curiosity into the glass-panelled coffin standing in the vestibule of the church. Inside the coffin lay an ancient mummified body, its skin was like dry parchment but its hair, teeth and nails were still in good condition.

The boy's mother was already inside the church, and when the boy had seen enough of the mummy he joined her. He glanced up at the west gallery and gave a piercing scream. Gazing down at him was a skinny figure wrapped in a shroud – a figure exactly like the dried-out body he had been studying a minute before.

For a moment the young tourist was paralysed with fear, then he sprinted out into the street and the reassuring roar of the traffic flowing from the Thames Embankment towards Billingsgate.

But it was not the only time that the ghost of Jimmy Garlick – as the mummy had long been nicknamed – had appeared. From time to time the shrouded figure was seen in the church and it was he who was blamed for the eerie sounds which sometimes echoed through the building.

The mummy had been discovered beneath the chancel before the original Church of St James had been destroyed in the Great Fire of London in 1666. No one knew how long it had been there or who it had belonged to, so it was put on display as a macabre attraction. Somehow it survived the flames of the London fire and when the new church was built to Sir Christopher Wren's design it was placed in the glass-panelled coffin.

It seems that it was this treatment of his body which caused the phantom to protest by making frightening appearances. If so his ghost should no longer trouble St James's because eight years ago it was decided to give Jimmy Garlick a proper burial.

There is an eerie tradition connected with a skeleton-like figure of Death holding a scythe which is carved on a tomb outside the Church of St Mary the Virgin in Barnard Castle, Durham. This is the figure in the photograph on the back cover of this book. The inscription on the tomb reads 'Here lies the Body of George the Son of Humphrey Hopper of Black Headley in Northumberland Derwent Water Gentleman who departed this life March 30, 1795 Anno Domini aged 23.'

This epitaph gives no hint as to why the tomb should be credited with a truly frightening power of prediction. If the skeleton's scythe is seen to move it means that the person looking at it, or a close relative of that person, is about to die.

A certain Mrs Hunt who lived in the area before the Second World War gave this account of the sinister tomb: 'My grandfather, a retired army officer, used to live near Barnard Castle. While home on leave, one summer morning he was passing St Mary the Virgin, when something whizzed past him. It was a raven. Looking in the direction whence it had come, his eyes lighted on the symbol of death, and, as he looked at it, he saw the scythe move. Thinking there was something wrong with his eyesight, he rubbed his eyes and looked again. The scythe was still moving, and he could feel the Figure of Death staring at him intently from its cavernous eyes.

'One of his men friends, chancing to see him gazing, asked him what he was looking at; and at the moment he spoke the scythe became stationary, and the sensation of being scrutinised ceased. The following week his father died suddenly.'

Chapter 16

The haunting of Willington Mill

'I must say it doesn't look very sinister, Edward,' said Thomas Hudson to his companion. The two young men were gazing at the bulk of a steam-driven flour mill, with a three-storey house beside it, silhouetted against the sunset.

'Tonight we may prove that the ghost of Willington Mill is a hoax,' replied Edward Drury. 'I have in my pocket a brace of pistols and I shall let one of them drop, as if by accident, in front of the miller to warn him not to play tricks upon me.'

'A capital idea,' laughed Thomas. 'Let us investigate the spooks then.'

They walked over a little bridge which spanned a watercourse bordering part of the house like a moat, and knocked at the front door.

A moment later it opened and a bearded man stood at the threshold.

'Good evening, sir,' said Edward. 'Are you the miller? I have permission from Mr Proctor. . . .'

'The miller lives in a cottage over there,' said the man with a smile. 'I am Joseph Proctor, the owner of this troubled house, and you must be the young doctor from Sunderland who wrote to me recently with such a strange request.'

'We are both interested in the world of spirits,' Edward said. 'And we are grateful for your permission to spend the night here.'

'You may get more than you bargained for, but being medical men I expect you are more hardened to unpleasant things than most. Let me show you the house. Because that canal outside is tidal this house has no cellars or passages under it which could be the cause of subterranean noise. But as you perhaps know it is not just sounds which afflict this house, distinct apparitions have been seen.'

'That we shall see for ourselves, Mr Proctor,' said Edward with a confident smile. 'At least, sir, I know you to be a respected member of the Society of Friends and whatever happens we will know that you are not likely to play a part in a deception.'

'There's no need to drop your pistol now,' laughed Thomas Hudson. 'Pray, lead on, Mr Proctor.'

The two doctors were shown over the lower rooms of the house and then led up the stairs.

'What form does the supernatural sound take, sir?' asked Thomas.

'There are heavy footfalls which have been heard to ring through the house during the hours of daylight as well as at night, though no visible presence has been seen which could be responsible for them,' explained Mr Proctor. 'Then sometimes there is the sound of tapping like a hammer hitting wood, chattering and jingling sounds and – strangely the most frightening of all – a mysterious noise like the mechanism of a clock being wound up. Ah, this is the third storey landing. You'll find the rooms up here rather bare, we – er – find it best not to use them. You are free to go into them as you wish, and you can lock the doors behind you to make sure that no human agency is responsible for any unusual phenomena you may witness. I bid you goodnight.'

When Mr Proctor had left them, the two friends searched the upper rooms, opening cupboards and making sure that all the windows were fastened. Then they sat on the landing and watched the weird shadows cast by their oil lamp. Time seemed to slow down as they puffed at their pipes and occasionally said a few words to each other. Although both wanted to give the impression that they were not bothered by the thought of anything supernatural, their ears strained for the slightest noise and when they did hear a normal creak from the woodwork they glanced nervously behind them.

'What is the hour?' Thomas asked after they had been on the landing for what seemed an age. Edward drew out his watch from his waistcoat pocket and held it close to the lamp.

'A quarter to midnight. . . .'

It was then that they heard the sounds. Afterwards Edward wrote: 'We both heard a noise, as if a number of people were pattering with their bare feet upon the floor, and yet so singular was the noise that I could not minutely determine from whence it proceeded. A few minutes afterwards we heard a noise as if someone was knocking with his knuckles among our feet; this was immediately followed by a hollow cough from the very room from which the apparition proceeded. The only noise after this was as of a person brushing against the wall coming up the stairs.'

But no one came up the stairs, at least no one that the two doctors could see.

As silence fell again the friends turned to each other. Both looked shaken.

'Well?' asked Thomas.

'Let's see it through until dawn,' Edward said. 'I'd hate to have to admit that I ran away from a noise.'

'I agree. And I can't remember a case of anyone suffering injury on account of *sounds*.'

From time to time Edward looked at his watch. The minutes dragged by but at least everything was quiet. An hour after they had heard the invisible footsteps Edward got up, yawned and said, 'I'm feeling cold, Tom. Think I'll go into that bedroom and lie down under a blanket. After all, if there are any more disturbances I can hear them as well lying down as shivering and getting cramp out here.'

'I'll come with you,' said Thomas, 'though I shan't go to bed until daylight.'

They went into the bare bedroom. Thomas slumped down in a chair and despite his intention to stay awake his head soon lolled forward. Edward sat on the edge of the bed and before lying down pulled out his watch yet again. It was ten minutes to one.

He put away the watch and suddenly he saw that the door of a closet was slowly swinging open. From the shadowy interior emerged a female figure draped in what appeared to be a grey shawl.

Speechlessly Edward Drury watched as the figure glided silently forward. Her head was bowed. Her left hand was pressed against her chest as though she was in pain, the right was extended towards the floor with her forefinger pointing downwards.

As the apparition approached the sleeping form of Thomas Hudson, her hand moved up as though to touch him. . . .

It was the danger to his friend that roused Edward into action. With a shout of warning he leapt forward, his own hands outstretched to protect him from the touch of the ghost. But he never reached it, he stumbled, fell forward on to his companion . . . and knew nothing more for three hours.

* * *

We know what happened that July night in 1835 at the haunted house, which stood between North Shields and Wallsend in Tyne and Wear, because Edward Drury wrote a full account of it for Joseph Proctor. Thomas Hudson also made a statement, part of which described what happened when Edward's shout of warning woke him up.

'His hair was standing on end, the picture of horror,' he wrote. 'He fainted and fell into my arms, like a lifeless piece of humanity. His horrible shouts made me shout in sympathy. . . . Mr Proctor and the housekeeper came quickly to our assistance and found the young doctor trembling in acute mental agony. Indeed, he was so much excited that he wanted to jump out of the window.'

The experience of the young men came as no surprise to Joseph Proctor. During the years between 1835 and 1837 he kept a diary in which he recorded the mysterious happenings which finally caused his family to leave their home.

The female ghost, said to 'have no eyes, only empty sockets', and a bald phantom resembling a priest were also seen by neighbours. These two apparitions started a legend that the woman, who had once lived in the house, wanted to confess a horrible crime she had committed at the mill but a priest refused to absolve her. After death their ghosts were doomed to return to the site.

An eye-witness description of the phantom priest was given by Thomas Mann, the foreman of the nearby mill who, with his wife and daughter and Mrs Proctor's sister, saw 'a bald-headed old man in a flowing robe like a surplice gliding backwards and forwards about three feet from the floor, level with the bottom of the second storey window'.

'He then stood still in the middle of the window and the part of his body which appeared quite luminous, showed through the blind,' Mr Mann said. 'In that position the framework of the window was invisible, while the body was as bright as a star, and diffused a radiance all round; then it turned a bluish tinge and gradually faded away from the head downwards.'

On 2 June 1835, Mr Proctor made a statement to a Mr Parker of Halifax by letter, declaring: 'The disturbances came to our knowledge in the beginning of the first month, but existed some time previously. There are several credible witnesses to the apparition of a woman in her grave clothes at four separate times outside the house.'

It was after this that Dr Edward Drury made his request to spend a night in the house with results which might have been fatal had not his friend prevented him leaping from the haunted room.

The author William Howitt became fascinated by the ghostly happenings at Willington. In a book he described the experiences of two young ladies who were guests in the house next to the mill.

One night their bed moved beneath them, another time it was violently shaken and the curtains lifted up and down several times. The following night they saw a female figure come out of the wall at the bed's head and lean over them before disappearing into the wall again.

There are many other accounts of the haunting which finally drove the Proctor family from the house in 1847. After that its interior was rebuilt to make flats for the millworkers and from then on reports of strange sounds became less and less, though the ghosts were seen at least twice after Joseph Proctor quit his home.

Chapter 17

The invisible hand

The editor of the *Ipswich Journal* re-read the letter which had just been delivered to him.

'Curious,' he muttered. 'Must be a joke – sort of thing we usually get for the first of April, though it's a bit late for that.'

He turned to his chief reporter.

'Know anything about a Major Edward Moor of Bealings House in Great Bealings?' he asked.

The journalist thought for a moment. He was proud of his local knowledge, having spent many years working in Suffolk.

'Major Moor? Ah yes, I know of him,' he said. 'He's an ex-officer of the East India Company's militia. I believe he rather distinguished himself out there and as a result was granted a special pension when he retired. He's a Fellow of the Royal Society and he spends his time writing about the Hindu religion.'

'Not the type to play practical jokes?'

'Rather not.'

'Take a look at this.'

The journalist quickly scanned the letter which was dated 5 April 1834, and which began: 'Sir, A

121

circumstance of unaccountable nature has recently occurred in my house. . . .'

'I'd say it's quite genuine,' he said. 'I mean, I'm sure Major Moor genuinely believed it happened. Whatever the cause, a letter like that always has entertainment value and we're bound to get some amusing comments in reply.'

'A Fellow of the Royal Society, you say,' mused the editor. 'At least that sounds respectable. We'll run it.'

When the major's letter appeared in the next issue of the *Journal*, news of it spread and for some weeks the country was fascinated by the mystery of who or what rang the bells at Bealings House.

It all began on Sunday 2 April when Major Moor returned home from a church service.

'Excuse me, sir,' said the cook, 'but something rather odd has been happening. Three times the dining room bell has rung, yet each time I went there there was no sign of what caused it. Well, you being out and the other servants having the afternoon off. . . .'

'Don't worry, cook,' said the major. 'There must be some simple explanation.' He went into the study and quickly forgot about the matter as he began working at his desk.

In those days all large houses had complicated systems of bells by which servants could be called to different rooms. When one of a row of bells jangled in the kitchen the servants would look up and, by seeing the number of the bell, know from where the summons came.

The next day Major Moor was reminded of the cook's words. Four times the bell connected to the dining room bellpull rang in the kitchen. The major was so intrigued by the unexpected sound that he waited in the kitchen for it to ring, then dashed to his dining room only to find it empty and undisturbed.

Perhaps there was something mechanically wrong with the wires and pulleys which worked the bell, he thought. Still it was odd. Even if there was a defect, *something* had to start the process off. . . .

The next day the major was convinced that something very strange was going on in his home. In the letter he sent to the *Ipswich Journal* he described the events of that Tuesday like this:

'I left home early, and returned before five in the afternoon. I was immediately told that "all the bells in the kitchen had been ringing violently". A *peal* at that moment sounded in my ears. I proceeded thither, and learned from the cook that "the five bells on the right" had, since about three o'clock, been frequently so affected.

'While I was intently looking at the bells and listening to the relation [account or story] that the rings had occurred at intervals of about a quarter of an hour, the same five bells rang violently; so violent was it that I should not have been surprised if they had been shaken from their fastenings. . . .

'During dinner the same five bells rang, perhaps every ten, twelve or fifteen minutes – and continued to do so, with nearly uniform violence, while the servants, six in number, were at dinner in the kitchen; and, with longer intervals until a quarter before eight when the last peal of Tuesday sounded. . . .

'. . . You and your readers may be assured that there is no hoax in the matter. I do not mean by me, but by anyone. I am thoroughly convinced that the ringing is by no human agency. . . .'

Even as the major wrote an invisible hand seemed to be plucking the bell wires. While he was at work in the breakfast room, with his son and grandson, and while there were four servants in the kitchen, the bells seemed to go mad at three or four-minute intervals. One was pulled with such violence that it hit the ceiling.

Many readers wrote to the *Journal* after the publication of the major's letter, some suggesting ingenious explanations for the bells' behaviour and some that the major was being tricked. Each time a batch of such letters was published he would reply to the points raised, once writing: '. . . my answer to some of their queries – that I keep no monkey – that my house is not infested by rats – that the wires of the five, and of the three, *pealers* are visible in their whole course, from their pull to the bells, save where they go through walls, in which the holes seem no bigger than necessary. . . . I have for many years of my life passed over large arcs of the earth's surface, and have seen divers tricks of distant people. If this be one, it surpasses all that I have seen. . . .'

Meanwhile as the days passed the ringing grew more and more alarming, and the major went to great lengths to make sure that he was not a victim of a hoax. Later he published a book on his experience entitled *Bealings Bells* in which he wrote: 'The bells rang scores of times when no-one was in the passage, or back-house, or house, or grounds, unseen. I have waited in the kitchen for a repetition of the ringing, with all the servants present – when no one – hardly "so much as a mouse" could be in concealment. But what matters? – Neither I nor the servants singly or together – nor anyone – be he whom he may came, could or can, however, work the wonderment that I, and more than half a score of others, saw. . . .'

The major said that the bells rang with a violence which, no matter how hard he tugged the bell wires, he could not imitate. He tried to get the effect by pulling the wires of the five 'pealer bells' where they ran along a passage between the back part of the house and the kitchen, but all the experiment showed was that if the wires were treated this way the bells would not ring at all. He came to the conclusion that the only explanation was a supernatural one.

For a total of fifty-four days Bealings House was haunted by the sound of bells which were not rung by human hand. Then the mystery ended as abruptly as it had started, leaving the major to write his book which was published in 1841. While writing it other cases of phantom bell-ringing came to his attention and he investigated thirty of these which he found to be as baffling as his own experience.

Today what happened at Bealings House would be put down to the work of a poltergeist. Although the dictionary defines it as a 'noisy mischievous spirit', many people believe that it is not a ghost but a mysterious force of energy which causes extraordinary things to happen, such as furniture to be shifted about a room and objects to be hurled through the air with great force. Such happenings have been photographed, and it is not unusual to read in newspapers about a house being troubled by a poltergeist.

England's classic case of supernatural sounds was attributed to the Phantom Drummer of Tedworth (now Tidworth, in Hampshire), but this also appeared to be the work of a poltergeist rather than a ghost.

William Drury, a wandering drummer, was brought before a magistrate by the name of John Mompesson on a charge of extorting money. When the magistrate examined his warrant to perform he found it to be a forgery and sent the man before a Justice of the Peace. The mountebank admitted his guilt, but asked for the return of his drum which was held in Mompesson's house. The request was refused until a report should be received from a colonel who had been the prisoner's commanding officer. Then the trouble began.

When Mompesson made a journey to London his wife was terrified by violent knockings about the house. On his return these unaccountable noises changed to the sound of drumming. At first it came from outside but later it echoed indoors. The family was kept sleepless for nights on end while the drum beat military tattoos or strange rhythms.

Neighbours often came to hear the phenomenon, and the fame of the Phantom Drummer spread so far afield that Charles II sent a Commission to look into the matter. While the investigators were at the house the drum remained silent, though it beat triumphantly when they left.

The activity of the poltergeist was not confined to the beating of a drum. The children of the house were teased by fingers they could not see, a family Bible was seized by an unearthly force and hurled into a fire and beds were fouled when the contents of chamber pots were poured on to them.

On one occasion John Mompesson, near the end of his tether through sleeplessness and anxiety, cried out, 'Satan, if the drummer set thee to work give three knocks and no more.' He was answered with three loud drumbeats.

During the disturbances William Drury remained in Gloucester jail. He was tried for witchcraft but acquitted for lack of evidence despite the fact that he had boasted, 'I have done it, I have plagued him, and he shall never be quiet until he hath made me satisfaction for taking away my drum.'

In the end he was sentenced to transportation for stealing a pig and the ordeal of the Mompesson family ceased.

* * *

Much more sinister is the phantom drumming which heralds the approaching deaths of members of certain old families.

Close to Harpham church in Humberside there is a well called the Drumming Well, and when the measured beat of a drum booms from its depths it means that death is about to claim one of the St Quentin family. The legend tells that a squire of that name was presiding at an archery match when a drummer named Thomas Hewson collided with him and toppled into the well. Another version is that the Lord of the Manor actually pushed him into the deep shaft in a fit of temper.

Unluckily for the squire, the drummer's mother had the powers of a witch and prophesied that whenever St Quentin's descendants were approaching death, her son would beat a ghostly drum.

A drum with a supernatural reputation and which once belonged to Sir Francis Drake is kept in Buckland Abbey near Plymouth. In 1581 Sir Francis acquired this thirteenth-century Cistercian monastery from the Glenville family. According to a well-known tradition, when Drake was on his death-bed he commanded that his drum, which had accompanied him on his voyage round the world, should be returned to the abbey. If sounded when England was in danger he would return to the aid of his country. The legend altered over the years until it was believed the drum would beat by itself to herald a war, and in 1914 it was said to have done so.

Chapter 18
The killer house

Winter fog shrouded London.

In Berkeley Square the wet pavement reflected splotches of sickly yellow light from the gaslamps, and the only sounds were the measured footfalls of a solitary police constable. He swept the doors he passed with the beam of his bullseye lantern to check they were secure, envying the families behind them who could enjoy their Christmas Eve in the bright glow of coal fires.

Suddenly there was a sound of someone running towards him. The constable turned and saw a young man in a sailor's clothes gesturing wildly.

'Come quickly, come quickly,' he panted, his face glistening with the sweat of fear.

'Now then, what's this?' asked the constable. 'What are the likes of you doing in a respectable area like this?'

'Me name's Robert Martin,' gabbled the sailor. 'Me and my mate are on Christmas leave from Her Majesty's frigate *Penelope*. We came up to London but we got no place to stay so we found an empty house to doss in. . . .'

'Not number 50!' cried the constable. 'Your mate

isn't still in there? Lord help him!'

With Robert Martin beside him he ran to where the halo of a street lamp dimly illuminated the 'To Let' sign by the open door of number 50.

'I woke up and saw it,' the sailor said. 'It was gliding towards Ted. . . .'

Suddenly there was a crash of glass, a wild cry and a body struck the spiked railings in front of the dilapidated building.

No one ever knew what had caused the sailor to leap to his death from an upper window that Christmas Eve in 1887. His friend stuck to his story about a 'whitish shape with two outstretched arms' – arms with talons rather than hands!

His account came as no great surprise. Victorian Londoners had long known that number 50 Berkeley Square was a house of particular evil. So sensational was its reputation that visitors to the capital made pilgrimages to the square to stand and stare at its grimy exterior.

At the end of the eighteenth century a certain Mr Dupre had confined his insane brother in an upstairs room. He was so violent that no one could handle him and he had to be fed through a special opening in the door. According to one legend it was the ghost of the maniac which became the Horror of Berkeley Square.

Other ghosts were seen at number 50. One of these was a child in a Scottish dress who had been frightened to death by a cruel servant in the nursery. Another was believed to be a young woman who had thrown herself out of an upper floor window. Her spectre sometimes hovered outside the window, tapping on the panes of glass.

In 1879 the April issue of the magazine *Mayfair* carried an article under the heading of 'The Mystery of Berkeley Square'.

'It appears that the house had an evil reputation for being badly haunted when it was last lived in,' it stated. 'One day a maidservant, newly arrived, was put to sleep in one of the upper rooms. An hour or two after the household was at rest, it was awakened by fearful screams from the new servant's room and she was found staring in the middle of the floor, as rigid as a corpse, with hideously glaring eyes – she had suddenly become a hopeless and raving mad-woman who never found a lucid interval wherein to say what made her so.

'The room was given up, but the house still remained occupied, and that seemed to be the end. But some little time afterwards, a guest arrived when the house had many visitors; and he volunteered for the room which all others were so shy of entering.

'It was arranged that if, after a certain time, he rang the bell for the room once, it was a sign that he felt himself as comfortable as could be expected; but that if he rung it twice, someone should come up and see what was the matter.

'At the end of the given time the bell only rang once, but presently the same bell gave a frantic peal; and those who ran to his aid found the ghost-defier a corpse where the girl had gone mad before. And dead men tell no tales.'

A man who scoffed at the idea of number 50 being haunted was Sir Robert Worboys. He was a hand-some young man-about-town whose country home was at Bracknell in Berkshire. When he visited London he stayed at the best clubs, and his adven-ture began one day in White's when the talk turned to London's haunted houses – and number 50 Berkeley Square in particular.

During the conversation Lord Cholmondeley introduced a man called Benson who actually owned the house in question. He was reluctant to discuss the matter, and Sir Robert suggested that it might be because – like himself – he did not believe in the supernatural. He replied that the manifestations at number 50 were so well known that he did not doubt them, and in fact had locked up the haunted room.

Sir Robert laughed so much at the idea that his friends challenged him to spend a night in the house if Mr Benson had no objection. Benson agreed providing that Sir Robert would be armed and that his friends would stay the night on the premises.

Sir Robert went to number 50 where he wished his companions goodnight and went up a flight of stairs to the fateful bedroom. There he lay down on the bed, one hand close to his pistol, the other near the bell-pull. Below in the drawing room, Lord Cholmondeley and several others dozed off.

At midnight the bell close to the drawing-room door began to ring. The startled men were climbing to their feet when a second peal jangled through the house. Mr Benson was the first up the stairs and was approaching the door of the bedroom when a shot rang out. Moments later he threw open the door of the bedroom to see Sir Robert Worboys lying across the bed, his head almost touching the floor.

Seeing his face in the lamplight someone cried, 'Cover him up!' His features were drawn back in an expression of sheer terror. At first it was thought he had shot himself, but when his body was examined there was no wound on it.

Another member of the aristocracy who volunteered to spend a night in the haunted room was Lord Lytton. He armed himself with two guns loaded with silver coins (silver was supposed to be a protection against evil spirits). After midnight he fired at 'something' which came at him out of the darkness, and

131

which fell 'like a rocket' before disappearing. It was this experience which inspired him to write a famous ghost story entitled *The Haunted and the Haunters*.

During the 1870s neighbours of the deserted house were alarmed by the sound of cries and the noise of heavy objects being dragged across bare boards, bells ringing and windows being slammed in true poltergeist fashion.

Towards the end of the last century another mystery was added to the story of number 50 Berkeley Square. A journalist wrote: 'The house . . . is uninhabited, save by an elderly man and woman who act as caretakers; but even these have no access to the room. That is kept locked, and the key being in the hands of a mysterious and seemingly nameless person, he comes to the house once every six months, locks up the elderly couple in the basement, then unlocks the room and occupies himself in it for hours.'

Nearly a century has passed since number 50 Berkeley Square enjoyed its ghostly reputation. Today it looks as respectable as its neighbours and is the office of a well-known firm of booksellers.

Chapter 19

Dorothy Forster

'In the night I suddenly found myself wide awake. I had the feeling that someone – or something – had banged into the end of the bed. At first I thought a person was actually moving in the room. I must admit I was very startled, and this gave me a sensation of fright. There was a sort of knocking. . . .

'The room was pitch black, and I lay for some time trying to summon up the courage to switch on the light. Perhaps I was afraid of what I might see if I did. But as soon as I did – the room was empty of course – the feeling of fear diminished and the awareness of a strange unseen presence in the room gradually left me.

'It was not until the next morning that I was told that this is the way the ghost manifests herself. Looking back on the experience I felt I had been foolish to have been frightened – I realised I had been left with only a deep impression of sadness.'

This account was given by a young woman who spent a night at the Lord Crewe Arms ten years ago. She was an artist who had travelled from London to the Northumberland village of Blanchland to draw the haunted hotel for a book illustration. Arriving late she was given a room in the tower of the ancient building. What she did not know was that it was to this tower the ghost returned.

Tired from a long drive, she went straight to sleep without any thought of the supernatural on her mind. The following morning she realised that the 'presence' which had woken her up was the gentle ghost of Dorothy Forster.

'In the haunted wing she manifests herself by a series of knocks,' the proprietor explained, 'and by gently shaking the bed of the occupant of the room. It seems this only afflicts ladies . . . it is as though there is something she wants to communicate to them.'

Sometimes the ghost is glimpsed at midnight, a white figure coming down the Old Hexham Road which descends between drystone walls from the Hexhamshire Common. She glides past Penny Pie Farm and some abandoned lead mines before vanishing in the direction of the Lord Crewe Arms which was once her home. Villagers say that she is most likely to be seen towards the end of September.

There is nothing sensational about this spectre of an eighteenth century lady – what is remarkable is the story behind it.

Born towards the end of the seventeenth century, Dorothy Forster was a member of a large Northumbrian family. Her favourite brother was the eldest, Tom, and while they were still young their mother died. When their father married again, Dorothy and Tom did not get on with their stepmother. They had an aunt, also named Dorothy, married to Lord Crewe the Bishop of Durham, and she became their affectionate unofficial guardian.

Thanks to her Tom was allowed to go to Cambridge University where he discovered that there was more to the life of a student than dreary study. After four terms he returned home a scholastic failure, but with plenty of stories of all-night drinking parties and gambling sessions. With him came a pleasant young man named Anthony Hilyard who had been his tutor.

Dorothy was delighted to have her brother back at the coastal village of Bamburgh, though she worried when he spent nights gaming with other young rakehells. In 1709 his losses on cards and horses brought him close to bankruptcy. At this point Aunt Dorothy saved him by persuading her husband to settle his debts in return for his estate.

The loss of his land did not depress Tom, and when his father retired from Parliament he took over his seat as member for Northumberland. It was as an MP that he began to take an interest in the Jacobite cause.

At the beginning of the eighteenth century many people believed that England's rightful king was not Protestant William of Orange, nor Protestant Anne who followed him, but Catholic James Edward. Known in history books as the Old Pretender, he was the son of James II, the last Stewart to wear the crown. The supporters of the Stewarts were known as Jacobites.

It was James Radcliffe, third Earl of Derwentwater, who encouraged Tom to join the movement. A year after his financial crisis Aunt Dorothy decreed that her niece and nephew should live in the old abbot's house at Blanchland. She believed such an isolated spot would protect the young man from being tempted back into his spendthrift ways. Lord Derwentwater lived close by at Dilston Hall and he spent a lot of his time with Tom and his sister.

Dorothy Forster found her stay in Blanchland the happiest period of her life. Her brother Tom was behaving himself and she had fallen madly in love with the handsome young earl.

* * *

If you visit Blanchland you will find a village where time has stood still. It was an abbey before Henry VIII closed down the monasteries and its houses were once part of the abbey buildings. The chapel where, long ago, monks prayed in their white robes is now the parish church, and the abbot's house is the local hotel. To keep its mediaeval appearance advertising signs are banned, only local stone can be used for building and the house doors are painted the same colour.

Blanchland has other phantoms besides that of Dorothy Forster. For the story we must go back to the fourteenth century when a savage Scottish raid threw the north of England into a panic. A band of Scots left the main force to plunder Blanchland Abbey, following an old drovers' track across Hexhamshire Common which was the abbey's only link with the outside world.

News of the coming attack must have reached the monks. When mist shrouded the common and hid the track they believed they had been saved by an act of God and pealed their bells in thanksgiving. The raiders followed the sound through the swirling whiteness and when the monks looked from their bell-ropes they saw their enemies appear like demons out of the fog.

An ancient cross in the churchyard next to the Lord Crewe Arms marks the burial place of the victims. For a long time it was said that, on the anniversary of the massacre, bells tolled by themselves and shadowy figures of the murdered monks moved among the graves.

It is still believed that on certain nights the spectre of the abbot, who was killed six hundred years ago, silently crosses the stone bridge spanning the River Derwent which flows past the village. While living at Blanchland Dorothy Forster was intrigued by this ghost and sometimes kept watch for him, little dreaming she would some day haunt the village herself.

Dorothy and Lord Derwentwater would have married if they had shared the same religion, but she was a Protestant and he a Roman Catholic and in those days the difference in belief split the country. Dorothy might have changed her faith for the man she loved had not the bishop reminded her that as his niece her first duty was to the Church of England.

The young couple put the problem to the back of their minds when they met at parties or went riding together. But at last they had to face the fact that – as neither would change from the religion of their families – marriage was out of the question.

Dorothy returned to Bamburgh where she lived sadly alone.

Two years later Queen Anne died and George I arrived from Hanover to ascend the English throne. Dorothy worried about her brother because she knew the new king would deal harshly with those interested in the Stewart cause. In January 1715, Tom Forster was expelled from Parliament, a warrant was issued for his arrest and only by hiding in the vaults of ruined Bamburgh castle did he escape the king's agents.

While Tom shivered in the dank dungeons the Jacobite rebellion broke out in Scotland. When the news reached Bamburgh, he and his sister rode secretly to Blanchland where they hoped its isolation would protect them from the troubles which lay ahead.

When they visited their old friend Lord Derwentwater he admitted he was involved in the rebellion. He wanted the son of James II on the throne, not a foreigner who could not even speak English. He declared that once the rebels came south of the Border and were joined by English Jacobites, English soldiers would not fight against them. He finally suggested to Tom that he should command the Northumbrian rebels.

Tom enthusiastically agreed, despite the fact his military experience was nil.

Soon he was riding at the head of three hundred armed men to join up with the Scottish rebels. When the combined army crossed the border into England near Carlisle he was appointed their official commander. From then on Tom was known as 'The Pretender's General'. It is believed he was chosen because English Jacobites were more likely to trust him than some 'foreigner' from Scotland. One can picture the young man aflame with the great adventure but as yet unaware of the horrors of war.

Tom led his army south to Penrith. Royal troops melted away without a shot being fired, allowing the Jacobites to collect much-needed weapons. They marched to Lancaster, and on to Preston where they were encouraged to learn that two companies of dragoons had retreated at their approach. It seemed Derwentwater had been right in his claim that English troops would not fight Englishmen, and the Jacobites rested for two days in the city – little dreaming that they were being encircled by a large army.

News of the enemy reached Tom Forster on Saturday, 11 November 1715. He ordered a detachment of rebels to march out and hold the Ribble Bridge while he and some of his officers rode ahead.

Soon they heard menacing drums, and from a vantage point saw a broad column of soldiers in red and white uniforms. The winter sun glittered on their bayonets and their disciplined movement struck dismay into the Jacobites. It seemed as though nothing could halt this well-drilled tide of royal power. It was probably at this point that the Stewart cause was lost – Tom Forster ordered his troops to withdraw from the bridge and return to Preston.

It was a fatal mistake because, with the river being unfordable, the bridge was the key to the town. The advancing troops could not believe it would be left undefended. The column halted warily and veteran soldiers scanned it anxiously. Was it mined? Would hidden cannons shatter it once they began to cross? Would they be slaughtered by musket volleys?

An order was shouted. The obedient ranks marched forward to the drummer boy's measured beat. But as the soldiers' boots rang on the bridge not a shot was fired and the men gave a cheer of relief as they realised the Jacobites had retreated. They were frantically digging trenches and throwing barricades across the streets of Preston.

The royal army's first attack was so fierce the rebels had to fall back from the outskirts of the town. Some dragoons took over two tall houses and harassed the defenders with sniper fire. In the streets Lord Forrester's regiment bravely advanced against heavy fire from the barricades. Scores of soldiers fell as they emerged from the smoke of fires lit to screen the Jacobites.

Although their casualties were light compared to the King's troops – only seventeen of Forster's men being killed, but two hundred of the King's – the Jacobites were disheartened when prisoners were captured. They were offered a chance to change sides and fight the hated German tyrant, but they answered to a man that they would remain loyal to King George. It was clear that the English were not going to support the rebellion as had been expected.

On Sunday the siege of Preston was reinforced by

more royal forces. This meant that the rebels' line of retreat would be cut off.

What made matters worse was that they did not know how to use the cannon they had brought with them. The Scottish rebels wished to sally forth and do battle in their traditional way with broadsword in hand. Soon English Jacobites were agreeing – better to fight their way out of Preston than wait while the enemy circle tightened upon them.

Such a desperate counter-attack never took place. Tom Forster, the Pretender's General, lost heart. Perhaps he was sickened by the slaughter, perhaps he felt the rebellion was lost and did not want to throw away more lives. Whatever the reason – and without a word to his followers – he told an unlucky drummer to sound the surrender and order all weapons to be laid down.

The rebels were shocked at hearing this proclamation above the noise of battle. One musketeer expressed their feelings by shooting the drummer dead. But Tom ignored the entreaties of his officers and continued with the capitulation. The rebellion, which became known in history as 'The Fifteen', ended with the capture of fifteen hundred Jacobites.

Anthony Hilyard, Tom's friend who had followed him faithfully through the rebellion, escaped from Preston in the confusion of the surrender. He made his way back to Blanchland and told Dorothy how her brother had been taken off to London in chains. She replied that they must set out for the capital immediately to ask her cousin Mary, the wife of the Lord Chancellor, to intercede on Tom's behalf.

Hilyard must have looked doubtfully at the snow-drifts piled up against the old abbot's house. To set out for London in this bitter weather would be madness. Not only was he exhausted after the campaign, but he did not believe anything could be done for Tom Forster. Having taken up arms against the crown the Pretender's General was destined for the scaffold.

Yet it is said that Anthony Hilyard loved Dorothy and – seeing her so distressed – he could not argue against her plan. He disguised himself as a blacksmith and Dorothy, posing as his sister, rode behind him on the cruel journey south through winter-bound England.

It took them three weeks to reach London. Dorothy went immediately to see her cousin, only to be told that she could do nothing for the man who had led an army against King George. All she did was obtain permission for Dorothy to visit him in Newgate Prison where, being a gentleman with money, he had good quarters. Dorothy made a point of always giving a very generous tip to the warder responsible for him.

While Dorothy waited to hear when her brother would stand trial, she received a note from her old sweetheart Lord Derwentwater who was imprisoned in the Tower of London. She went and bade him a sad farewell just before he was beheaded on 24 February 1716. His death made Dorothy realise Tom's plight – if an earl was not to be spared, what chance did a commoner have? And, to add to the horror, only a noble could expect a merciful stroke of the axe. It was likely that Tom would be hanged, drawn and quartered. To Dorothy it was clear that she must arrange his escape.

Anthony Hilyard was astonished at the efficiency with which this young woman, from remote Northumberland, planned the operation. On her next visit to Newgate she broke down in tears before the friendly warder as he was escorting her from Tom's room.

'I wish I could help you, my lady,' he said.

'But you can,' she answered and outlined the plan of escape, secretly terrified in case the man should report her to the governor.

'How much?' was his only question, and it was settled that he would assist her for five hundred guineas. During her next visit she was able to slip Tom a master key which had been fashioned from a wax impression supplied by the warder. Then she waited at the Salutation Inn in Newgate Street where Hilyard had stabled four thoroughbred horses.

On 10 April Tom invited Mr Pitts, the prison governor, to dine with him. In the past Pitts had enjoyed his prisoner's conversation and his wine. Now he raised a glass to him and said how he regretted they had to meet in such dismal circumstances. Toast followed toast and as the bells rang for midnight Tom asked his valet to fetch more wine.

The man went off with the head keeper's servant who was responsible for the wine cellar key. As the servant entered the vault he heard the door slam behind him and the key turn in the lock.

Meanwhile Tom – whose experience of heavy drinking paid off this night – asked to be excused while he went to the toilet. Pitts nodded and drifted off into a tipsy doze. Some minutes later he opened his eyes and gazed blankly round the empty room. A moment later he was wide awake as he realised that his prisoner had not returned. He stumbled to the door, and found it had been locked by the master key which had also unlocked the gaol's street door.

Outside Dorothy and Hilyard had been waiting for Tom and his valet with the four fast horses. Soon they were galloping through the night to Rochford where the ship Dorothy had hired was waiting to cast off.

Dorothy Forster and Anthony Hilyard returned to Northumberland, happy in the knowledge that Tom, now an exile in Rome, need no longer fear the gallows. Yet, as they approached Blanchland, they realised that everything had changed. All that remained of Dorothy's old life was the faithful Hilyard.

Legend says he wanted to marry her but she gently rejected him. Afterwards her uncle gave him a position at Durham Cathedral. According to the inscription on her portrait, which hangs in the Lord Crewe Arms, Dorothy later married a man named John Armstrong of Berryhill, and died in 1767.

Something still draws Dorothy back to the village where she spent her happiest days. Unlike other phantoms in this book her ghost is not spectacular – but it is certainly the ghost of a super lady.

Chapter 20
Knock, knock!

'I tell thee it were like the groanings of a dying man,' said the maidservant.

'Oh, Nanny Marshall, what a wicked woman you are to be sure, making up such lies to frighten us poor girls,' said one of the seven Miss Wesleys who were listening to the maid's story.

'Tell us what else happened, Nanny,' cried another. 'Did a skeleton's hand grasp you by the neck?'

The girls giggled as Nanny continued seriously, 'Something caused the upstarting of my hair, and made my ears prick forth. . . .'

Her words were drowned by shrieks of mirth. Had the young ladies not been the daughters of a clergyman, they might have allowed themselves to roll on the floor in their merriment. Little of interest happened at Epworth, a village surrounded by dreary fens in the area now known as Humberside, and the maid's silly story of a ghost was as good as a play.

Little did the sisters know that soon they would find the silly story far from funny.

They were the daughters of the Reverend Samuel

Wesley. He was also the father of John Wesley who became the founder of Methodism. The Reverend Samuel had arrived at Epworth at the close of the seventeenth century. He was soon on bad terms with his congregation who were Presbyterian-minded and heartily disliked their Church of England vicar.

At one stage the clergyman was so unpopular that some of his parishioners burnt down his home but this disaster made him more determined to do what he believed was right. He built a new house of brick which, as Epworth Old Rectory, is a place of pilgrimage for Methodists today. It is this rectory which was the scene of one of England's most believable hauntings — no one believed the Wesleys could tell anything but the truth.

It was on 1 December 1716 that Nanny Marshall heard the sounds which made her 'ears prick'. Soon afterwards other members of the household were aware of mysterious noises. On 2 December the vicar's servant, Robert Brown, was sitting with one of the maids in the dining-room. Just before ten o'clock both heard a knocking at the door which led into the garden. Robert got up and opened it, but there was nobody there.

He probably blamed local children for playing a trick, but as he turned back into the room it began again.

He looked out a second time. Again there was nobody to be seen. He closed the door and immediately there came three heavy blows which made the panel shake. This time Robert flung it open so fast that if someone was playing a trick there would be no time for them to hide. But as before — nothing!

Alarmed and puzzled, the servants went up to bed. In his garret Robert was just dozing off when he heard a noise like the gobbling of a turkey cock. It was followed by the sound of someone stumbling over his boots. What made the servant's heart beat faster was the fact that he had left his boots downstairs.

Next evening one of the Miss Wesleys experienced the haunting. Her brother John wrote '. . . between five and six o'clock, my sister Molly, then about twenty years of age, sitting in the dining-room reading, heard as if it were the door that led into the hall open, and a person walking in, that seemed to have on a silk nightgown, rustling and trailing along. It seemed to walk round her, then to the door, then round again; but she could see nothing.'

After that the occupants of the house, apart from the Reverend Samuel, were uncomfortably aware that an unseen intruder was among them.

By now the girls had forgotten how they had mocked poor Nanny. They kept together, not wishing to be alone when 'Old Jeffrey' – as they christened the ghost – was about. And soon it was not only eerie sounds which made them shudder, small objects travelled through the air by themselves.

What alarmed the girls most was the fact that their father had not experienced the strange phenomena. It was an old fenland superstition that in such a haunting the person who did not hear the knockings was marked for death!

The Reverend Samuel snorted at the suggestion. Indeed he pooh-poohed the whole idea of the ghostly sounds.

'It's some of the ungodly members of this parish,' he declared. 'They tried to burn us out, now they're trying to scare us away . . . or perhaps,' and here he looked closely at his daughters, 'my own children are having some fun at my expense.'

At this the young Miss Wesleys were furious. They declared that they wanted Old Jeffrey to continue with his noises until their father heard them for himself. And the next night the Reverend Samuel had his first taste of the supernatural. He was jerked out of a heavy slumber by nine very loud knocks which sounded right by his bed. As he sat up the air was filled with sounds of rapping and banging, and then, in the words of the vicar himself, 'a noise in the room over our heads as if several people were walking'.

In writing to her son Mrs Wesley said that the disturbance 'was so outrageous that we thought the children would be frightened; so your father and I rose, and went down in the dark to light a candle. Just as we came to the bottom of the broad stairs, having hold of each other, on my side there seemed as if somebody had emptied a bag of money at my feet; and on his, as if all the bottles under the stairs (which were many) had been dashed in a thousand pieces. We passed through the hall into the kitchen, and got a candle and went to see the children, whom we found asleep.'

The Reverend Samuel had to admit that there was something supernatural going on under his roof, but he was not ready to accept that Old Jeffrey was a ghost. Being a clergyman of his day, he was inclined to think that the Devil had something to do with the disturbances.

'Ride over to Haxey and ask the Reverend Hoole to come to Epworth as soon as he can,' he told Robert Brown. 'Together we shall exorcise the evil from this place.'

When the vicar of Haxey arrived he could hardly believe his ears. The Wesley girls were all talking at once about someone called Old Jeffrey, the servants kept looking over their shoulders as though in a perpetual state of fear, and to cap it all the Reverend Samuel was explaining the need to hold a service of exorcism. To the Reverend Hoole it seemed that the household had gone mad – until he became aware of Old Jeffrey himself!

The Reverend Samuel had planned to conduct the exorcism the following day and asked his colleague to stay overnight at the rectory. When the Haxey vicar joined the family for evening prayers he was startled by a noisy interruption at the point where his host began a prayer for King George. The knocking sounded so loud it suggested that Old Jeffrey had no respect for the monarchy.

As the Reverend Hoole carried his candle to his bedroom he was a worried man. It seemed that the Wesleys had not gone mad after all. He'd actually heard the knocking – and in the middle of prayers! But could it be a ghost, some sinister earth-bound spirit lurking in the home of a respectable Church of England clergyman? No, it was preposterous!

He climbed in his bed and was about to blow out his candle when he thought better of it. The truth was that the Reverend Hoole was afraid of ghosts!

The night which followed was the worst of his life. He had only just dozed off when the air about him seemed to reverberate with unearthly noises.

Bang, bang bang! came Old Jeffrey's knocking. Not another wink of sleep did he get, and at dawn he had his horse saddled up and left for his home parish as fast as the animal could go over the frozen road.

The Reverend Samuel had to intone the service of exorcism alone, but Old Jeffrey refused to be cast out. From then on he became more frightening, especially when members of the family started to see *things*. It began one evening when Mrs Wesley saw something suddenly appear from under a bed, dart across the room and vanish. Her sister Emilia, who was with her, described it as something 'like a badger, *only without any head. . . .*'

Robert Brown saw the same apparition a little later, also something white, about the size of a rabbit, which 'turned round before him several times'. Once he was grinding corn when he was suddenly aware that the handle of the hand mill was turning by itself.

A more alarming aspect of the haunting was the disembodied force which pushed members of the family after nightfall.

'Thrice I have been pushed by an invisible power,' wrote the Reverend Samuel, 'once against the corner of my desk in the study, a second time against the door of the matted chamber, a third time against the right side of the frame of my study door.'

But the most spectacular of Old Jeffrey's tricks occurred one night when Nancy Wesley sat down on a bed to play cards with some of her sisters. Suddenly the bed was lifted from the ground.

'Surely old Jeffrey will not run away with me,' cried the girl as she leapt to the floor. A few moments later the bed was back in its usual position.

'Come on, play the game,' said the other girls. 'You should be used to Old Jeffrey by now.'

'I don't think I'll ever get used to him,' muttered Nancy as she cautiously sat down again. Immediately the bed rose in the air again, dropped to the floor and then lifted and fell several more times. Again Nancy jumped off and nothing would persuade her to continue with the game.

Two months after Nanny Marshall had first reported hearing dismal groans, Old Jeffrey suddenly quit Epworth Old Rectory. Slowly the Wesley family returned to normal life though the puzzle always remained – what was it that had haunted their home?

Chapter 21

Sukie, the Jibber and Charlie

'I did not realise at the moment when it happened it was a ghost,' said Dorothy Boon. 'I was looking for the young lady who worked in the kitchen. . . . She slept in a room in the staff quarters so I went to find her. I opened the door and it was just on the tip of my tongue to say, "What's the matter with you, Pat?" She was sitting on a stool looking into the fireplace, all hunched up and appearing to be very miserable. As I looked at her more closely she just disappeared!'

What Mrs Boon had seen was the White Lady who has haunted The George and Dragon of West Wycombe in Buckinghamshire for the last two centuries. Her story was a tragic one, and she is known to the pub's staff as 'Poor Sukie'.

In life Sukie was a sixteen-year-old servant at the inn. She had long blonde hair, and she was said to be very vain of her looks. Her airs and graces sometimes irritated the other members of the staff and they teasingly called her 'Your Ladyship'. Three West Wycombe boys were in love with her, but although it amused her to play them off against each other, she confided to her friends that she was going to marry somebody more important than a village lad.

Sukie thought perhaps her Prince Charming had appeared when an unknown gentleman reined up his horse at The George and Dragon. From his clothes he appeared to be rich, his manners were elegant and his face was handsome.

She was attracted to him immediately, and made sure that she was the one who served him when he ordered a meal. When she took him a treacle pudding, she was so nervous that she did not watch what she was doing and put her thumb in it. Part of the crust fell on to the young gentleman's clothing, and Sukie removed the sticky crumbs with her handkerchief. This little accident made them both laugh, and soon they were chatting in a friendly fashion.

Today, whenever there is a mishap in the kitchen of The George and Dragon – such as a hole appearing in the pastry – the staff blame it on Sukie's phantom thumb.

Again and again the young gentleman came to the inn to have a meal and joke with Sukie. Although she did not learn his real name, it was rumoured that he was a nobleman, and in her dreams the girl could imagine herself being properly called 'Your Ladyship'. . . .

Meanwhile the three lads, who had lost their hearts to her, watched the flirtation from the bar. Before they had been rivals, but now Sukie's interest in the stranger united them. Over their ale they planned a trick on her which would give them a taste of revenge and remind her of her station in life.

A message was sent to her purporting to come from the mysterious stranger. It asked her to meet him in the nearby chalk caves the next night, and added that she should wear a wedding dress. Poor Sukie, she had visions of him taking her away for a romantic marriage ceremony.

The caves mentioned were really tunnels which

had been cut into the hill overlooking West Wycombe, and it was here that members of the Hell Fire Club used to meet. Its founder Sir Francis Dashwood had the passages quarried to provide employment for men who were out of work following a series of harvest failures. Today you can explore the caves where once politicians and men of fashion met for wild parties away from disapproving eyes.

Wearing a white dress, Sukie slipped out of The George and Dragon the following night to keep the appointment which she hoped was going to alter the course of her life. She entered the tunnel system carrying a lamp but instead of finding the handsome young man she saw the three village yokels who laughed drunkenly to see her in her wedding gown.

Sobbing with disappointment and angry at the cruel trick which had been played upon her, she picked up lumps of chalk and hurled them at her tormentors. At first they continued to poke fun at her, but when several of the chalk fragments had found their mark they too became angry. They pushed her roughly from one to another, and then spun her round until she was dizzy.

Sukie reeled across the floor of the cave and collapsed, fracturing her skull against the rock wall. The sight of her motionless body sobered up the three youths. Hoping that she was merely stunned, they carried her back to The George and Dragon where they managed to enter her room silently and lay her on the bed. Then they sneaked away to their homes.

When Sukie did not appear for work next morning someone went to her room – and found her dead.

Soon after the tragedy stories began to circulate that her phantom, wearing a white wedding dress, had been seen at The George and Dragon and at the place where she met her death. And it has continued to appear down the years.

In 1967 an American journalist wrote about an experience he'd had at the inn. He described in the *Reader's Digest* how, while staying at The George and Dragon, he was awakened by a feeling of cold fingers touching his face. He pulled a light-switch cord and found that the sensation vanished as light flooded the room, but when it was switched off again the caress of the cold hand returned. After this had happened several times he saw a pinpoint of light floating a metre above the floor near his bedroom door.

It had an 'opaque pearly quality' and continued to grow until it was 60 centimetres in diameter and 120 centimetres high, but when he again tugged the light-switch cord he found the room to be empty. As with the sensation of the fingers, the mysterious glow returned the moment when the electric light was switched off. He summoned up the courage to get out of bed and investigate further. As he walked towards the door he encountered a zone of intense cold – his breathing became difficult, his limbs felt heavy and for a wild moment he wondered whether he was suffering from a heart attack.

As he stood there he was swept by another feeling – a sudden depression which, he claimed, was a sympathetic feeling towards the ghost. He felt that 'life must have felt like this for poor Sukie with no one to protect her dignity'. Then the luminous thing 'ballooned' towards him, causing him to leap back into bed and switch on the light.

The George and Dragon also has a haunted staircase. It is haunted by the invisible ghost of a guest who was murdered in an upstairs bedroom long ago. The details of the crime have been forgotten, but the sound of footsteps on the stairs continues.

* * *

Another very old inn haunted as a result of a murder has the sinister name of the Caxton Gibbet. It is situated by a roundabout on the A45, close to Caxton village in Cambridgeshire. The grim-looking gibbet which inspired its name still stands beside it.

According to the old tradition connected with the inn, a landlord's son went into a bedroom occupied by three travellers who had drunk more than their share in the bar. The young man's plan was to rob them while they snored but, while he was going through their belongings, one of the guests woke up and saw him. As he opened his mouth to shout for help the thief killed him.

Realising that the other two men could give evidence against him if they woke up, he murdered them while they slept. One at a time he then dragged their bodies into the yard and dropped them down a well. But this did not save him. The bodies were discovered, the young man was arrested and hanged from the gallows which stood by his father's inn. He is believed to have been the last prisoner to be hanged there.

In the haunted room an eerie presence can make the temperature drop suddenly. Another ghostly manifestation is the sound of footsteps moving about the inn late at night, presumably those of the murderer as he dragged his victims' corpses to the well.

There are plenty of other grim tales associated with the Caxton Gibbet. In the eighteenth century a man committed a brutal murder in a place known as Monk Field, after which he fled to America. He stayed there seven years, then homesickness forced him to return to England – and Caxton where he had spent his boyhood. With money earned in America he was able to spend his time drinking at the inn where one day he drunkenly bragged about his violent past. The result was that he was arrested, identified by a birthmark as the Monk Field murderer and sentenced to be hanged from the Caxton gallows.

Soon after the execution a baker was passing the inn when he noticed that the criminal left hanging from the gibbet – as was the custom in those days – was showing signs of life. The noose of the hangman's rope had not tightened enough to strangle him. The kindly man pitied the unconscious prisoner and cut him down. Then he tried to revive him and when the victim opened his eyes he gave him some bread to chew in the hope that this would help him revive.

For this Christian act the baker himself was arrested and was the next to swing from the arm of the gibbet.

In 1753 the son of another landlord of the ill-omened inn took part in a mail robbery and was caught soon afterwards. He, too, was executed at Caxton and his body was left dangling for five months as a dreadful warning to others.

The gibbet remains but the rope which used to hang from it has been removed. Not so long ago a youth stood on a box under the gallows arm and put his head through the noose. For a joke his friends kicked away the box, and the gibbet almost claimed another victim.

A different form of hanging was responsible for the haunting of England's most unusual pub – The Grotto at Marsden on the coast of Tyne and Wear. It is unusual because – apart from being haunted by a thirsty ghost – it is set in caves at the bottom of a thirty-metre cliff. In the old days visitors to The Grotto reached it by walking along the beach or toiling down Jack the Blaster's stairs. Today you can descend by lift to the modern building which stands in front of the old caverns.

Smugglers hid their contraband in them, and later they were used by a miner known as Jack the Blaster. He came to work at the Marsden quarries in 1782 and when he and his wife found the local rents too expensive they moved into the caves. To reach his natural home more easily the Blaster cut steps into the cliff-face, and soon he and his family were one of the curiosities of the neighbourhood. He was quick to cash in on this, enlarging the caves and selling beer as an inn-keeper.

Later a man named Peter Allen, nick-named The Hermit, took over the caves. He and his wife had eight children, and he carved extra rooms for them out of the limestone. He also hewed a ballroom out of the solid rock for the entertainment of local people. During his excavations he unearthed eighteen skeletons, some of which were thought to be the remains of smugglers.

The inn was modernised in 1938 and it is in the lounge bar that the haunting takes place. A landlord explained that a special Georgian pewter tankard was kept in the bar for the ghost to quench his supernatural thirst.

'If the beer is left in anything but this particular tankard he won't touch it,' he said. 'And he certainly shows his annoyance. Sometimes in the morning the place looks as though a tornado has struck it. Chairs knocked over and all that sort of thing. So at night we leave the tankard full of beer on the bar and everything is peaceful again. It's a sort of offering to the ghost of the smuggler who died here, though how a spirit can consume beer I don't understand.'

The tale of Jack the Jibber, the thirsty ghost of The Grotto inn, goes back to the days when smugglers used to land their goods at night on the shore beneath the cliff.

One night a lugger was approaching with a cargo of illicit tobacco when the waiting gang noticed that one of their number was missing. For some time he had been suspected of treachery, so the boat was warned off by a gunshot. Soon afterwards excise officers appeared but could find no evidence to convict the gang.

It was not long before the smuggler, who had hoped to earn a reward by betraying his comrades, was caught and taken to the caves. He was placed in a tub which was hauled up to the high rocky ceiling by a rope normally used for lifting contraband. It was too high for him to jump, and there he had to remain. The smugglers lowered him once a day to give him food and water.

Then the gang quit the cave. Perhaps the excise men were on their trail, or perhaps they decided finally that death was a fitting punishment for the traitor. Whatever the reason, one can imagine the growing terror of the prisoner when no one came to give him food. As the dark hours dragged by his ears strained for the sound of seaboots on the rough stone floor but he was never to hear that sound again. He remained trapped beneath the roof until thirst released him from his torment. In some mysterious way the agonising desire to drink has remained with the ghost still known as Jack the Jibber.

Not all of Britain's haunted inns have such grim traditions. Many have ghosts who are quite mischievous and who are even regarded with affection by landlords and pub staff. An example is the phantom which returns to the Holman Clavel near the village of Blagdon in the Blackdown Hills of Somerset. The six-hundred-year-old inn was once used as a resting place for monks on pilgrimages to Glastonbury Abbey.

It is believed that the spirit which attached itself to the Holman Clavel is that of a monk who was expelled from his order – perhaps because he stayed on at an inn instead of continuing his pious journey. Over the generations he has been nicknamed Charlie, and it is agreed that he is a jolly ghost who enjoys playing poltergeist-type pranks.

'Things disappear and then turn up months and months later,' said the landlord. 'Once the key of a box disappeared. It was missing for two or three years and then one morning there it was, right in the middle of the carpet on the floor of the bar.'

Charlie was blamed for a recent prank played on a cameraman who had been filming the inn for television. He declared that, having finished work late at night, he was certain that he locked his gear in the car boot before driving off. But when he reached his home he discovered he did not have his camera or a single piece of his filming equipment. It was all found standing in the pub's car park when he anxiously returned the next morning.

A member of a local radio station saw Charlie while staying at the Holman Clavel in 1970. When he arrived at the inn he knew nothing at all about its resident ghost but he swore that one night he was awakened by a noise and saw the figure of a monk appearing to float in the corner of his room. For long seconds he lay petrified, then summoning up his courage he leapt out of bed and snapped on the light. When he did so the figure disappeared.

Charlie's most common manifestations are connected with the ancient skittle alley at the back of the inn. The game must have been popular with the monk because late at night there comes the rumble of balls being bowled at the ninepins, yet when anyone goes to see who is playing everything is in its place.

A photographer who visited the inn was very interested in the haunted skittle alley and asked John Clapp the landlord if he would pose with a ball at one end while he took a photograph from the other.

He made a point of choosing a spot well to one side of the alley, knelt on one knee and focused his Rolleiflex.

'Send down a ball so I can get an action shot,' he called.

The landlord did as he was asked, sending the three-kilogram hardwood ball rolling down the alley. He aimed it down the side of the alley opposite to the photographer to ensure there was no danger of him being hit. But halfway down the alley the ball unaccountably changed course. It was as though it had been deflected by an invisible hand. Before the photographer could dodge the ball, which he saw swerve towards him through his viewfinder, it struck his right kneecap with an agonising impact.

Did the phantom monk resent the photographer invading his domain with his camera and change the course of the ball to teach him a painful lesson? Painful it certainly was because today, several years after the accident, he still limps if he has to walk up or down stairs.

The author of this book can vouch for the story – he was the photographer.

More Beaver Books

We hope you have enjoyed this Beaver Book. Here are some of the other titles:

Haunted Castles A Beaver original. Spooky stories of over 80 castles all over Great Britain related by Mark Ronson, with maps and a detailed gazetteer explaining how to find those castles that are open to the public and a black and white photo insert which depicts the settings of some of the most fascinating tales

Haunting Tales A collection of stories about all kinds of ghosts and strange happenings which is guaranteed to send shivers down your spine, by authors such as M. R. James and Algernon Blackwood. Compiled for older readers by Kathleen Lines

The Beaver Book of Horror Stories A Beaver original. A spine-chilling collection for older readers by such master horror writers as Ray Bradbury and H. P. Lovecraft; edited, and with a specially written contribution, by Mark Ronson

These and many other Beavers are available from your local bookshop or newsagent, or can be ordered direct from: Hamlyn Paperback Cash Sales, PO Box 11, Falmouth, Cornwall TR10 9EN. Send a cheque or postal order made payable to the Hamlyn Publishing Group, for the price of the book plus postage at the following rates:
UK: 45p for the first book, 20p for the second book, and 14p for each additional book ordered to a maximum charge of £1.63;
BFPO and Eire: 45p for the first book, 20p for the second book, plus 14p per copy for the next 7 books and thereafter 8p per book;
OVERSEAS: 75p for the first book and 21p for each extra book.

New Beavers are published every month and if you would like the *Beaver Bulletin*, a newsletter which tells you about new books and gives a complete list of titles and prices, send a large stamped addressed envelope to:

Beaver Bulletin
The Hamlyn Group
Astronaut House
Feltham
Middlesex TW14 9AR

206289